Flowers
of Jamaica

Flowers
of Jamaica

Monica F. Warner

MACMILLAN
CARIBBEAN

Macmillan Education
Between Towns Road, Oxford OX4 3PP
A division of Macmillan Publishers Limited
Companies and representatives throughout the world

www.macmillan-caribbean.com

ISBN 0 333 97523 5

First published 2004

Designed by Amanda Easter
Illustrated by Tessa Eccles
Cover design by Gary Fielder at AC Design
Cover photographs by Monica F. Warner

Front cover: Bell Flower (*Portlandia latifolia*)

Back cover: Century Plant (*Agave sobolifera*)

Printed and bound in Thailand

2008 2007 2006 2005 2004
10 9 8 7 6 5 4 3 2 1

Contents

Dedication

To my husband George
For the steady encouragement and hands-on participation that made the pursuit of plants such fun.

Acknowledgements

I am greatly indebted to Dr. C.D. Adams for the detailed and helpful editing of the manuscript. Many thanks are due to Dr. G.R. Proctor and Mr. P. Lewis both of the Life Sciences Department, University of the West Indies at Mona, Jamaica, and Camille Webster and other personnel at Hope Gardens, Kingston for their assistance in locating and identifying specimens. I also wish to express my gratitude to all those who showed such interest in my flower gazing and spontaneously offered their much-treasured nuggets of information. Finally, my thanks to old friends Alick and Sarah Jones and Nick Gillard of Macmillan Publishers for being the founders of the project.

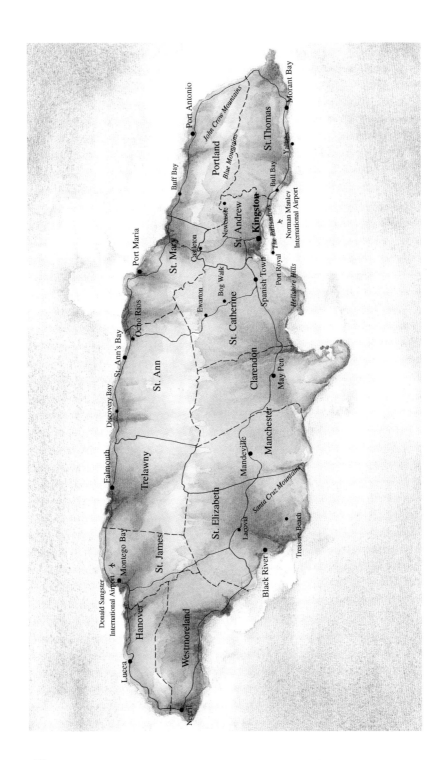

Introduction

Jamaica is a relatively small island in an altogether gorgeous setting. Surrounded by the blue Caribbean Sea, the island rises in a series of dramatic mountain ranges to a high point of over 7 350 ft (2 240 m) at its eastern end. The spread of habitat provides room for many different kinds of plants, and flowers blaze from the coasts upwards. All newcomers notice this diversity rather quickly. For example, those travellers who disembark at the Norman Manley International Airport on the south coast on their way to Port Royal or the capital city Kingston, will be driven along a narrow strip of land called The Palisadoes. They will pass through dry, sandy areas where typical desert plants, thorn scrub, cacti, milkweed shrubs, agaves and other succulents grow. Mangrove species fringe the sides of the road and cover small islets. A 20 minute drive up into the hills behind Kingston will take them into the wet, forested zone. Here mosses, ferns and wild ginger plants cling to the steep slopes. Trees are bearded with Spanish Moss and are host to many other epiphytes. There are about 3 000 species of flowering plants in the wild and nearly one third of these are endemic to the island, that is they originated and occur naturally only in Jamaica. As this country is hundreds of sea miles away from any major continental landmass, the remaining majority of the plant species are, of necessity, those native to the region and those introduced by the early explorers, colonists and traders.

Many of the plants introduced to Jamaica were also taken to other Caribbean islands and similar tropical places around the world.

Visitors from temperate countries will recognise many of their cold weather plants thriving in the higher, cooler regions of the island. These include the globular, blue heads of Agapanthus lilies, flowering Rhododendron, Azalea and Hydrangea shrubs. There are also Nasturtium vines trailing typical red and yellow blooms and Peach trees which flower and fruit satisfactorily at the correct altitudes. The humbler Dandelion weeds and prickly Gorse bushes are frequently found at elevations over 4 920 ft (1 500 m). The reverse is also true. Keen gardeners from abroad have been delighted at the sight of tender pot plants such as Hibiscus and Bougainvillea growing to riotous size and flowering gloriously all year round.

Jamaica was once famous for its historic Botanical Gardens. The Royal Botanic Gardens – known as Hope Gardens – in urban Kingston, St. Andrew, and Castleton Gardens, snug in the mountain valley of the Wag Water River just over the border in the parish of St Mary, are the two largest and most accessible survivors. Although they have fallen on hard times, both these gardens remain popular and worthwhile places to visit. There are, of course, newer establishments such as Shaw Park Botanical Gardens at Ocho Rios and Cranbrook Flower Forest, which is between Ocho Rios and Discovery Bay on the north coast. These latter two gardens lie some height above sea level and afford spectacular views of the coastline from their respective approach roads.

Jamaicans have maintained an enduring connection with their floral heritage. Virtually all homes, hotels, parks and other public places have their complement of flowering plants designed for pleasure and shade and also to provide fresh fruit and vegetables. However, many Jamaican people continue to make firm distinctions between weeds and bush plants and those considered worthy enough to be planted in their gardens and put into vases.

A handful of plants have the prefix 'Duppy' attached to their local names: plants such as Duppy Cherry and Duppy Gun. Duppies are essentially ghosts: spirits of the dead. They are wide-ranging entities and embody the likes of witches, elves, goblins, fairies, trolls and so on. Duppies exert a powerful influence on the national psyche. Plants whose features show some resemblance to ordinary, everyday objects or things are often given the names of these things. Then the label 'Duppy' is added to emphasise the distance from normality and to suggest that these features can be of use only in the spirit world, for example, 'Duppy Machete' and 'Duppy Basket'.

Naming

The plants are identified by a series of names: their common or local names (and alternatives), the family name and the scientific, international names in Latin. The scientific name consists of a unique pair, the genus and species names. The four examples given below illustrate some of the relationships between plants.

Common name	Family name	Genus and species names
Okra	MALVACEAE	*Hibiscus esculentus*
Sorrel	MALVACEAE	*Hibiscus sabdariffa*
Seaside Mahoe	MALVACEAE	*Thespesia populnea*
Cerasee	CUCURBITACEAE	*Momordica charantia*

Taxonomy is based on the sum of the differences and similarities between plants. To the casual observer okra and sorrel plants, and their flowers in particular, have much in common; so much so that they share the same family (Malvaceae) and the same genus (*Hibiscus*). Seaside Mahoe has only enough similarity to share the family name (Malvaceae), while Cerasee, being completely different, has a wholly unrelated set of names. Cerasee, however, does resemble other members of the Cucurbitaceae family, the melons and cucumbers. Closely related plant families are grouped into orders and so on. There are about 300 families of flowering plants worldwide.

Those interested in a more detailed look at plant identification (taxonomy) should know that texts on the matter usually include the name of the botanist(s) who first described and named the plant. This is shown by the following examples: Sorrel, *Hibiscus sabdariffa* L., where L. stands for Linnaeus; and Mexican Vine, *Antigonon leptopus*, Hook. & Arn., where Hook. stands for Hooker and Arn. stands for Arnott.

Where there have been changes in nomenclature arising from continuing research, I have given both sets of scientific names as follows: currently accepted name and synonym.

Orchids

Potted and cut-flower exotic orchids are seen all over Jamaica, the result of a thriving horticulture. There are also over 200 species growing in the wild but, like other prized objects, they suffer from over collection. There are several publications solely dedicated to the identification of orchids and I have decided, with one exception, to exclude this complex family from the book because of the relative scarcity of most native species.

The Flower

As plant lovers everywhere are gratefully aware, there is a dizzying diversity in shape, size, colour and form in any assemblage of different blooms. This section outlines the blueprint common to all flowers and brings the major deviations to notice.

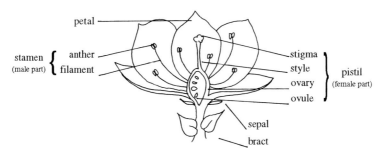

Fig. 1: *Parts of a typical regular flower*

Flowers are the reproductive parts of plants. In essence, pollen produced by the **stamens** is transferred to (**pollination**) and united with (**fertilisation**) the **ovules** in the **ovary**. This union produces the seeds and the ovary swells to form the fruit. With their bright colours, enticing scents and shapes, flowers attract humans, insects and other animal life. This attention helps to spread first the pollen, then the fruit (and therefore the seeds) to new places. Under the right conditions seeds will germinate and grow to form new plants.

There are many variations built around the basic flower structure and reproductive plan. These include the following:

- Irregular flower structure, e.g. Pea-type flowers of the Fabaceae family
- Separate male and female flowers on the same plant, e.g. Castor oil
- Separate male and female plants, e.g. Pawpaw (Papaya) and Long John
- Petals reduced to small, insignificant structures, e.g. Bougainvillea
- Bracts, sepals or leaves becoming large, bright and petal-like, e.g. Bougainvillea and Poinsettia
- No useful seeds produced and new plants obtained from bulbs (lilies) or root and stem cuttings (Gingers and Hibiscus).

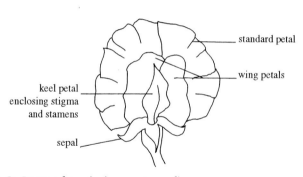

Fig. 2: *Parts of a whole pea-type flower*

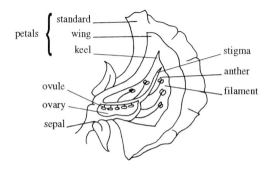

Fig. 3: *Section through a pea-type flower*

Types of Plants

Vines and **creepers** may have woody or soft stems, which in both cases are too weak to fully support the plants. They can be annual or perennial. Short-lived plants with soft stems are often described as herbaceous. **Shrubs** are perennial, woody plants. They are generally smaller than trees, have shorter life spans and are sometimes multi-stemmed. Trees are among the largest, living organisms. Each, typically, has a single, woody stem and many branches. **Trees** continue to grow larger each year and, if permitted, they can live for a very long time. These broad and useful divisions are not absolute, they may overlap. For instance, the distinctions between large shrubs and small trees are not always clear-cut.

Arrangement and Content

The plants in this book are presented by family. All the plants are grouped into their respective families. These are then listed in order of their botanical relationships starting with the herbaceous **monocotyledons** (*Strelitziaceae* to *Orchidaceae*) and going on to the more advanced and often woody **dicotyledons**. Within the family, plants are arranged alphabetically by genus. For each plant I have provided as many of the following details as I could: photograph(s), scientific and common names, place of origin, a description, type and habitat as well as other points of interest such as local use.

This book is designed to be a quick pocket guide to the 115 or so common flowering plants and a single genus (two species) of orchids, chosen by the author. These include endemic, native and introduced plants growing wild or under cultivation. Other compilations of common Jamaican flowering plants will, of course, contain many different examples.

I hope that visitors and islanders alike will now be tempted to rush to the garden or take to the mountain trails, leafing through the book naming and enjoying the many beautiful and fascinating flowering plants of Jamaica.

The Flowers

◆ STRELITZIACEAE

Strelitzia (*Strelitzia reginae*)
Other names Bird of Paradise, Crane Flower, Queen's Flower

Strelitzias are South African in origin and are closely related to the Banana family. They are cultivated here for their exotic, bird-like blooms. *Strelitzia reginae* can grow to around 5 ft (1.5 m) high. It has stiff, pointed leaves that are pinkish-red at the midribs and edges. Each flowering stalk elongates then bends and swells to form a single, beak-like platform or sheath. The remaining flower parts slowly emerge from this base. First, there are the bright orange, petal-like units (sepals) followed by the blue, winged, stamen tube or tongue. As each flower fades and dies back a new one emerges erect from the sheath. *Strelitzia reginae* produces about eight blooms per cycle. The tree form, *S. nicolai*, produces correspondingly large, white flowers in multiple, boat-like bracts. Both plants bloom throughout the year.

Strelitzia reginae

◆ HELICONIACEAE

Wild Banana (*Heliconia spp.*)
Other names Wild Plantain, Lobster Claw

Like their relations the Banana plants, Heliconias can rapidly sucker into tall thickets of supple, 3 ft (1 m) long leaves. Amongst this forest of foliage and soft stems can be found the most amazing inflorescences – they may be erect, hanging, spirally arranged or flattened. However, they all consist of a series of big, colourful bracts that contain the smaller flowers and fruit. Hummingbirds frequently visit these bracts to feed on the plentiful supply of nectar. Heliconias are cultivated domestically and commercially. Their architectural blooms fetch high prices on the cut flower market. A few grow wild in shady woodland. *Heliconia rostrata* and the several forms of *H. psittacorum* are popular with the owners of smaller gardens. There are a vast number of different types of Heliconia all now housed in this single genus of the Heliconiaceae family. The majority of these exotic flowering plants are native to Central and South America and the West Indies.

Heliconia rostrata

Heliconia psittacorum

Heliconia wagneriana

◆ ZINGIBERACEAE

Red Ginger (*Alpinia purpurata*)

These tall, leafy perennials come from the Pacific Islands. They have found great favour in private gardens, parks and other public places. The plants are guaranteed to spread quickly by underground stems, and fill many an awkward or difficult place in the garden since they also bloom well in the shade. Red Ginger plants have long, lance-shaped, upwardly slanting leaves arranged alternately along each cane-like stem. Eventually the stems bear short, terminal, flowering cones, which consist of closed bracts or scales. The cones elongate and the, by now, petal-like, red bracts fall open to reveal (in a few cases) small, white, tubular structures. These are the true flowers. An average flower head is about 9 ins (23 cm) long, but some do evolve into pendulous, branched, 'S'-shaped structures. Clusters of new plantlets with roots (bulbils) frequently develop from the fading flower heads. Both the Red Ginger and the less common pink form make attractive, long-lasting cut flowers.

White Ginger Lily (*Hedychium coronarium*)

White ginger lilies are natives of South Asia. They are moisture-loving plants and grow at mid-altitudes within the eastern half of the island. The tall, slender canes bear strap-like, pointed leaves and terminate in short, green, cone-shaped flower bracts. Each stunning, all white bloom is butterfly-shaped and cream-green at the throat and appears from June to December. Together, the flowers emit a heady perfume.

Wild Ginger Lily (*Hedychium gardnerianum*)

The fragrant, mass flowering of Jamaica's wild, mountain ginger lilies is due in large part to *Hedychium gardnerianum*. Discovered, originally, in the Himalayas, the plants have naturalised here and now rampage over sections of the hills above Kingston. The sturdy, 6 ft (2 m) tall canes sprout long, supple, blade-shaped leaves. These slant upwards and are arranged alternately about the stem. Eventually, in late summer, the stems develop impressive, terminal flower heads. Most are less than 12 ins (30 cm) long but they can attain double that length. Each inflorescence is studded with dozens of sweet-smelling, yellow flowers. Rows of crimson stamens projecting from the blooms create the distinctive, spiky appearance.

◆ CANNACEAE

Canna (Canna spp.)
Other names Canna Lily, Indian Shot

Cannas are tropical American garden plants whose bright and cheerful flowers have been favourites for decades. The cane-like stalks, big, alternately arranged leaves and running, underground stems (rhizomes) are similar to their close relations the bananas and gingers. Massed *Canna* blooms have been used to great advantage in municipal parks and gardens. There is now a wealth of different forms and colours as well as the parental reds and yellows. The plants grow 3–6 ft (1–2 m) tall and terminate in clusters of three-part flowers. The small, warty fruit produce many hard, black seeds, which resemble the 'shot' used in old-fashioned guns. Each shoot dies after flowering but there is always a handful of suckers eager to replace it. Species like the small-flowered *Canna indica* and *C. coccinea* now commonly grow wild.

◆ LILIACEAE

Single Bible (*Aloe vera*)
Other names Sinkle or Sinkel Bible, Bitter Aloes, Sempervivum

Because the soothing extracts of this plant have found a place in the vast, international cosmetics industry *Aloe vera* is now almost a household name. These are Mediterranean plants that grow naturally in dry areas at, or near to, sea level. Like all Aloes, which are principally South African, they consist mainly of rosettes of long, barbed, sword-like leaves that branch from short, creeping stems. Each plant produces a mass of tubular, yellow blooms along the top third of a 3ft (1m) tall inflorescence. *Aloe vera* plants are also cultivated as garden ornamentals and for use in indigenous herbal remedies. The bitter, jelly-like transparent sap is easily removed from the plump leaves and widely used to treat burns and make hair, skin and dietary preparations. The peculiar 'Single Bible' names are thought to be derived from Sempervivum – a separate family of hardy, Alpine succulents. Flowering is best in the first half of the year.

◆ ARACEAE

Anthurium (*Anthurium andraeanum*)

Anthuriums are wonderful, ornamental imports from Central and South America. They are rather curvy, sensually-contoured plants that are highly popular as potted specimens and long-lasting cut flowers. All Anthuriums share the same heart-shaped leaves and distinctive, two-part flower plan. Each has a large, brightly coloured, shield-like bract called a spathe from which sprouts the spike (spadix) bearing a packed mass of small, inconspicuous flowers. Red spathes are the most common although several other colour varieties exist. Wild forms have less showy, green spathes.

◆ AMARYLLIDACEAE *Onion family*

Easter Lily (*Hippeastrum puniceum*)
Other names Amaryllis, Lent(en) Lily, Red Lily

Easter Lilies actually bloom from late winter to early summer. They are bulb-rooted, strap-leaved plants that are native to tropical America. Here in Jamaica, they will thrive at sea level but are most heavily cultivated and naturalised in the central upland parishes. These popular, large-flowered lilies are available in several shades of red. They last wonderfully well as cut flowers. Each hollow, flowering stalk grows between 1 and 2 ft (30 and 60 cm) tall and bears the clusters of spreading, greenish-throated blooms.

Spider Lily (*Hymenocallis latifolia*)

Spider Lilies are also bulb-rooted, tropical American plants that grow naturally along coastal areas. There are a handful of other species some resident at higher locations. *Hymenocallis latifolia* flowers several times per year. When this happens a long, stout, hollow stalk grows up from the clump of strap-like leaves, and bears a clutch of pencil-thin, erect buds. The buds open serially, revealing exquisitely scented but short-lived blooms. Each stalked, star-like flower has six, slender, white segments. The bases of the equally long, orange-headed stamens are held together in a filmy, cup-like web. Sniff too closely and you get a dust of orange pollen on your face.

◆ AGAVACEAE *Sisal family*

Century Plant (*Agave sobolifera*)
Other names Coratoe, Karato, Maypole

These impressive plants are native to Jamaica and Cayman Brac. They can grow in large numbers in parched, limestone areas such as the Hellshire Hills. Each consists of a huge rosette of succulent, barbed, sword-shaped leaves, which may measure 6 ft (2 m) long by 10 ins (24 cm) wide. Despite being called Century Plants, these Agaves flower well before they are 100 years old. After years or even decades of growth, a towering, pole-like inflorescence emerges in late spring. The stalk may be as much as 30 ft (9 m) tall and carries the flowers at its upper regions. The orange-yellow blooms resemble large, upturned pads borne at the ends of short, alternate branches. They appear to consist largely of bristling stamens. The entire plant dies after flowering but not before producing numerous plantlets called bulbils in its inflorescence. These will grow into future generations. The related *Furcraea hexapetala*, which grows further inland, shares the same three local names. It has creamy-white, cup-like blossoms that hang from the flowering branches.

Wild Scallion (*Trimezia martinicensis*)

Trimezia martinicensis is a moisture-loving, wild Iris common only in damp places some way above sea level. It has recently charmed its way into local gardens where it can survive and flower even in dry shade. The plants have long, pointed, strap-like leaves and even when flowering, they remain less than 3 ft (1 m) in height. Each flowering stem carries two to four yellow, three-part blooms. They each have three large and three small petals arranged alternately. All are mottled brown towards the throats of the flowers. New plants regularly bud from the old flower stalk. This wild Iris is also found in Central America, Brazil and some other Caribbean islands.

◆ ORCHIDACEAE

Bletia (*Bletia florida*)

Bletia florida grows naturally in Cuba and on the banks and cliffs of upland Jamaica where it remains largely unnoticed until flowering time. Then it is a delight to discover the wands of purplish, thimble-sized blooms. The plants are usually leafless at this stage and bear their nodding, three-part blossoms along slender, 3 ft (1 m) long flowering stalks. *Bletia purpurea*, highly similar, is more widely distributed in the Caribbean and parts of tropical America. It has distinctively 'chinned' buds that mature into marginally smaller, lighter-coloured flowers. Bletia orchids have long flowering seasons both in the wild and as plants in pots.

Bletia florida

◆ ARISTOLOCHIACEAE *Dutchman's Pipe family*

Duppy Basket (*Aristolochia elegans,* syn. *A. littoralis*)
Other name Calico Flower

The exotic blooms of *Aristolochia elegans* hang from slender vines like tiny tubas in single file. These climbing, Brazilian plants were originally garden imports that migrated to the wild to grow in rough pastures and thickets. Their broad, heart-shaped leaves are arranged alternately along the stems. Each oddly-shaped bud consists of two inflated bladders of unequal size that are connected by a short, slanting tube. The larger, outer unit will blossom into a 3–4 in (6–10 cm) wide, circular corolla beautifully patterned with purple markings on a white background. It leads by way of a sharply-angled turn into the smaller, green coloured sac, which contains the reproductive parts. These curious blooms entice small insects into their inner chambers. Inside, the tiny creatures will pollinate the flowers which eventually develop into hard, ribbed capsules up to 2 ins (5 cm) long. When mature, each partially splits to form a six-part, hanging basket and releases its crop of many, flattened seeds. Flowers and fruit are produced for the best part of the year. The double-sized flowers of *A. grandiflora* emit a foul odour as insect bait. This species is also called 'Duppy Flytrap' or less attractively, 'Poisoned Hog Meat'. *A. ringens* is popularly known as 'Dutchman's Pipe'.

Aristolochia elegans

◆ POLYGONACEAE *Seaside Grape family*

Mexican Vine (*Antigonon leptopus*)
Other names Coralilla, Coralita, Coral Vine

Mexican Vines are tough, climbing plants that flourish throughout lowland Jamaica, beside streams and gullies as well as on dry, sandy heaps along the coast. Crinkly, triangular leaves are borne alternately on the ridged stems. Each heavily-veined leaf is associated with either a tendril or a flowering stalk at the same location. The vines regularly throw a pleasing veil of green followed by sprays of pink flowers, over hedges, fencing, unsightly waste plots, and other unadorned landscapes. They also dangle daintily from the branches of trees. Some flowers open fully to reveal five petals and a mass of yellow stamens; most, however, remain closed and budlike. They are at their best towards the end of the year when the blooms are brighter and there are more of them. Although Mexican Vines appear to spring spontaneously from bare earth, they are in fact perennial plants that have edible tubers underground the size of small eggs. White-flowered vines are less common. Green leaves and stems picked from non-flowering plants are used to make a tea for treating chesty complaints. The plants are, of course, natives of Mexico.

Triplaris americana (female)

Long John (*Triplaris americana*)
Other names Ant Tree, Ant Wood

Long Johns are cultivated, ornamental trees from South America whose smooth, lean trunks may exceed 66 ft (20 m) in height. They have a distinctive dark-grey bark that peels away to expose pale-coloured patches. The heavily-veined leaves are arranged alternately on the branches and can be up to 16 ins (40 cm) long and all point downwards. At maturity, Long Johns carry their spiky, plume-like inflorescences well above the heads of many other trees. Flowering occurs during winter and spring when the trees become laden with bloom. Male trees carry densely-packed spikes of tiny, cream-coloured flowers. Female spikes are feathery and consist of dozens of much larger, pink to red, three-part blooms. Trees in bloom of either gender are highly attractive. They may be confused with mangoes (*Mangifera indica*) which are in flower at the same time, but Long Johns are columnar whereas mango trees have a more rounded outline. The name *Triplaris*, relates to the female flowers and salmon-brown fruit it produces. Each fruit comes equipped with three, long blades with which it spirals to the ground from above.

◆ **AMARANTHACEAE** *Callaloo family*

Cockscomb (*Celosia argentea*)

Cockscomb plants are cultivated ornamentals that have spread around of their own accord. They are herbaceous, tropical annuals which generally grow to about 4 ft (120 cm) tall. Their pointed, green leaves have a variable inlay of rusty red. The much-branched older plants bear many plume-like, pink-coloured flower spikes in an attractive candelabra fashion throughout the year. The plumes become more silvery-white with age but they retain their sleek, purplish tips. There are several other garden varieties including those that have the comb or crested flower heads.

◆ NYCTAGINACEAE

Bougainvillea (*Bougainvillea* spp.)

Bougainvilleas are delightful and widely-grown ornamental plants, which came originally from South America. They are colourful, prickly, woody shrubs or climbers occurring now in dozens of different varieties. Although the plants flower more or less all year, they are particularly exuberant during the dry season when their branches can be awash with a froth of paper-thin blooms. Each consists of three brightly coloured bracts that surround an equal number of smaller, true flowers. Both bracts and leaves are somewhere between oval and triangular. Bougainvilleas are available in a vast number of different colours, from the common reds and purples through to orange, pinks, yellows and whites. The popular bi-coloured form called 'Surprise', bears magenta and white flowers on the same stem. Some varieties can soar 30–40 ft (10–13 m) up a convenient tree from which tumble spectacular cascades of bloom.

Four o'clock (*Mirabilis jalapa*)

Other names Marvel of Peru, Morning, Noon and Night

These entertaining, South American garden plants now largely grow wild. They are short, sprawling, leafy shrubs that often blanket roadsides in damp, upland districts in vegetation. The shrubs bear soft, paired, pointed leaves and slender, tubular flowers. Each flower may be over 2 ins (5 cm) long and terminates in five, free petal lobes from which protrudes a delicate spray of stamens and stigma. The flowers are fragrant and are most commonly rose-coloured, though pink, orange, yellow and white forms do also exist. Unfortunately, these elegant blooms only open at about 4 o'clock in the afternoon and close at sunrise! The small, hard, black-skinned objects that are later found nestling in the ring of sepals are the ripe fruits.

◆ CACTACEAE

Cactus (*Cereus hexagonus*)

This cactus is one of a group of similar-looking garden plants that are native to the south Caribbean and northern South America. They produce many column-like branches that start from a short, thick and rounded main stem. The newest members possess a downy, blue-green sheen. Each succulent column of *Cereus hexagonus* is scored by four to six deep grooves and the whole is stoutly defended by groups of sharp spines growing on the corresponding ridges. A common variant has twisted stems which spiral out from the centre. These plants flower enthusiastically in late spring and then on and off for the rest of the year. The stalked, pointed buds open at night to reveal white, conical blooms of a delicate, lily-like beauty. Each scented saucer-sized flower fades by sunrise the following morning. The resulting oval fruit can be as big as an orange and becomes red when ripe.

◆ CRASSULACEAE

Leaf of Life (*Bryophyllum pinnatum*, syn. *Kalanchoe pinnatum*)

These small succulents are natives of Madagascar. Here, in Jamaica, they are common bush plants with a preference for dry hillsides. The thick, paired, pale-green leaves carry a succession of buds in their purple-lined and scalloped edges. Therefore, at leaf fall, dozens of new plantlets appear. Flowering lasts from December to May when the plants develop stalked inflorescences some 1–2 ft (30–60 cm) tall. The stems bear clusters of unusual, hanging, purple and green buds. The inviting, gas-filled bladders, (closed calyx tubes) are liable to be 'popped' by delighted children. When mature, the buds open allowing the tips of the four, dark red petals to emerge. Country folk have many uses for the fleshy leaves. They are often brewed to make a tea for colds or eaten raw with salt to promote general well being. Freshly-chopped leaves are also used as a poultice.

◆ CAESALPINIACEAE *Cassia family*

Poor Man's Orchid (*Bauhinia variegata*)
Other names Bull Hoof, Butterfly Tree

Bauhinia variegata is an ornamental tree, one of several widely planted *Bauhinia* species. They are appreciated both by humans and hummingbirds for their orchid-like, nectar-filled blooms. Each large flower has five, stalked petals and a curving, elongated bundle of stamens and pistil or just a single stamen in the case of the pink-flowered *B. monandra*. Flower colours range through shades of pink, scarlet and purple to white. These small to medium-sized trees are collectively called 'Bull Hoof' here because of their foliage. All the plants bear light-green, two-lobed leaves that resemble the cloven hooves of cattle. Elsewhere, *Bauhinia* leaves are likened to camels' feet. The leaflets close at night. Most 'Bull Hoof' trees are natives of tropical Africa and Asia. The indigenous *B. divaricata*, locally named 'Mocho John', has delicate, almost shredded pink and white flowers. They are a fraction of the size of the cultivated blooms. These shrubs grow naturally in thickets and woodlands on limestone. The deep purple *B. blakeana*, emblem of Hong Kong, is featured on its coins.

Bauhinia variegata

Bauhinia monandra

Bauhinia divaricata

Dwarf Poinciana (*Caesalpinia pulcherrima*)
Other names Pride of Barbados, Peacock Flower

These prettily-flowered but thorny shrubs are probably indigenous to Central America and the West Indies. They are widely grown as hedging but are seen just as often thriving in roadside thickets. The plants form airy, branching shrubs 6–10 ft (2–3 m) tall and have attractive, bi-pinnate foliage. The upright inflorescences bear cherry-headed buds that develop into flowers with five petals. One of these has a tubular stalk. The blooms can be red or yellow, but, most frequently, they are a combination of both colours. Each flower carries a delicate, elongated, spray that is made up of the slender stamens and pistil. The resulting fruit are distinctive, flat, red-brown pods.

Candlestick Cassia (*Cassia alata*)
Other names Christmas Candles, King of the Forest,
Ringworm Bush

Candlestick Cassias begin to light up around November when the plants start flowering. They then produce long, upright flowering stalks which terminate initially in club-shaped, orange-coloured inflorescences. The buds successively shed their orange bracts and open fully into striking, golden-yellow flowers. The resulting winged pods go black when ripe. These 6 ft (3 m) tall shrubs are from tropical America and flourish here in gardens and in the wild. Their long, pinnate leaves lie almost horizontal. Each bears seven to nine pairs of large, light green leaflets. The shrubs are just as widely-known as 'King of the Forest' and their leaves are much appreciated by local people as a source of a good bush tea for colds and blood pressure. Pounded leaves and plant sap are also used to treat ringworm and other skin rashes.

Golden Shower Tree (*Cassia fistula*)
Other names Cassia Stick Tree, Indian Laburnum

Golden Shower trees are native to tropical Asia. They can grow between 30 and 40 ft (10 and 13 m) tall and for most of the year they function as ordinary shade trees. Then, beginning in early summer these Cassias are transformed into something of a floral feast. The trees develop long, tapering inflorescences that hang from near leafless branches. The bouquets contain dozens of large, yellow flowers. Each scented bloom is 2–3 ins (5–6 cm) wide, has five petals and contains a clutch of yellow-stemmed, brown-headed stamens. Three of these are elongated and curved like the prominent, green, sickle shaped pistil. Later on in the long flowering season, the blooms are complemented by the returning bunches of young foliage. Each pinnate leaf is made up of around five to eight pairs of large, lime-green leaflets. The persistent fruit, which are cylindrical pods, can be 2–3 ft (60–90 cm) long. They are packed full of seeds like pills in a tube. These pods have prompted the name of 'Pudding Pipe Tree' in India.

Golden Shower Tree (*Cassia fistula*)

Siamese Cassia (*Cassia siamea*)

Cassia siamea is a robust tree native to the Far East. The evergreen plants are fast growing and quickly become tall trees that are well covered with dusty-green foliage. There are about eight pairs of small, oval leaflets to each pinnate leaf. These Cassias are usually planted to provide roadside shade. The trees bloom and fruit patchily during summer becoming somewhat ragged-looking during the process. Each substantial, upright flowering spike bears several, well-spaced clusters of round buds which open in succession. The resulting flat, yellow flowers have five sepals and petals each, ten sturdy brown anthers and a curving, green pistil. Their narrow, ribbon-like pods grow to between 8 and 10 ins (20 and 25 cm) long. Pink-flowering species like *Cassia javanica* (*C. nodosa*), Pink or Javanese Cassia, are much less common in Jamaica.

Cassia siamea

Poinciana (*Delonix regia*)

Poinciana (*Delonix regia*)
Other names Flamboyant, Flame tree

Poinciana trees flame into their scorching best from June to September. Branch after bare branch blooms with masses of large, scarlet, orange or yellow flowers. One of their five, clawed petals is always lighter – almost white. Originally from Madagascar, Poincianas are now among the best loved and most commonly distributed of Jamaica's famed flowering shade trees. They have widely spreading branches and can reach 40–60 ft (13–16.5 m) in height. The attractive, ferny foliage gradually reappears and the fruits mature into long, flattened, woody pods. They remain dried on the tree for a very long time occasionally being rattled by the breeze. Trees like this have always doubled as outdoor schoolrooms. Poinciana's beautiful blooms are the National Flowers of Puerto Rico.

Jerusalem Thorn (*Parkinsonia aculeata*)

These are attractive, wispy, small trees. They are natives of tropical America that are well established along dry, southern, coastal areas. Their drooping habit, reduced leaf area and clustered blossom bear resemblance to the Broom shrubs (*Fabaceae*) of temperate regions. Each pinnate leaf is about 12 ins (30 cm) long and consists of a slender rib bearing one to two dozen really tiny, paired leaflets. Mass flowering occurs in spring and summer but some of these pretty flowers are borne on and off all year. The yellow blossom blooms in small groups towards the ends of the branches. Four of the five petals are crinkly, yellow units while the prominent fifth is spotted red. Most flowers develop into short, flat pods. The trees tend to be planted along roadsides in tough environments as they carry fearsome, 1 in (3 cm) long thorns, useful equipment to help ward off collateral damage from troops of grazing animals. Intriguingly, Jerusalem Thorn trees are called 'Madame Yass' in Haiti.

Yellow Flame Tree (*Peltophorum pterocarpum*)

These are ornamental trees imported from the vast region described as South-east Asia to North Australia. They are attractive on all accounts – form, foliage, flowers and fruits. Mature specimens are grand trees, rising 65–75 ft (20–23 m) in a spreading, domed shape, each covered in a luxuriant growth of doubly-pinnate, ferny leaves. Flowering can be profuse and very long lasting. The sturdy, branched inflorescences bear flowers typical of the family, each with five, stalked orange-yellow petals, brown anthers and prominent pistil. These blooms contrast beautifully with the green foliage and striking coppery growths that are each a mass of tender, young pods. The Yellow Flame Tree is at least partially deciduous during winter and spring.

Woman's Tongue Tree (*Albizia lebbeck*)

Albizia lebbeck plants are native to the tropics of the Old World. They were first obtained in 1782 from a captured French ship. The vessel was on its way from the Indian Ocean also carrying such well-known items as Mango plants (variety Number 11) and Jackfruit. The shrubs grow naturally in dry places by the roads and on hillsides and will proliferate in the arid limestone forests where they have become invasive. They can attain 40ft (12 m) in height and a good spread, especially when grown as specimen shade trees in schoolyards, parks and grounds. The plants produce tight heads of hard, round buds. These open into balls of fragrant, spiky, cream-green flowers that last only a short while before collapsing into bedraggled fluff. *Albizia lebbeck* plants are well covered in sprays of doubly-pinnate leaves which are arranged alternately. Each midrib bears five to seven small, oblong leaflets. It flowers and fruits from April to September losing much of its ferny foliage in the following dry months. Indeed, the trees can be recognised by their numerous, dry pods which are a pale, sandy colour, and so flat and transparent that the seed placements inside are clearly visible. The pods seem to hang on indefinitely, rustling cheerfully as the wind blows, hence the common name, 'Woman's Tongue Tree'.

Mimosa (*Calliandra inaequilatera*)

These graceful, open shrubs bear pairs of doubly-pinnate leaves that sit widely apart on the many, outwardly arching branches. Each leaf has only two sets of small, close-packed leaflets that close as the sun sets. Mimosa blooms resemble floral powder puffs or pompoms. A single one consists of a mass of small, inconspicuous flowers whose incredibly long, slender stamens make up the 'puff' we see. This example is only one of many pink, red or white, large-flowered ornamentals that come from Central and South America. The wild species in Jamaica, which include three endemics, grow in thickets or on limestone cliffs. Their smaller flowers are usually white or tinged with yellow or green.

Shame-o-Lady (*Mimosa pudica*)

Shame-o-Ladies are small, prostrate South American weeds now common in pastures, roadsides and other places with a sunny outlook. They are rather prickly plants, having feathery, pinnate leaves and pretty, pink balls of minute flowers. The foliage is sensitive to pressure and a simple touch or harsh breeze will cause instant collapse of the leaf stalks and closure of the leaflets. This reaction is temporary, as all plant parts will unfurl before long. Jamaicans of all ages find fun demonstrating this reaction. The leaflets also close at night.

furled

unfurled

Guango Tree (*Samanea saman*)

Guango Tree (*Samanea saman*)
Other name Rain Tree

Guango trees come from South America. First planted here only on pasture land, they are now a feature of Jamaican landscapes from plain to forest. The stout-stemmed, mature specimens are constructed on a grand scale. They may be over 50 ft (15 m) tall, and are rounded, layered and spreading all at the same time. This provides a remarkably open infrastructure that is roofed over by a tracery of small leaflets. The canopy is therefore unusually porous to rain especially at night when the leaflets close. Wild pines often cluster along the tops of near horizontal branches while bunches of other epiphytes dangle from beneath. The trees flower freely in spring and autumn adding a delicate layer of tufty, pink-white blossom. Guango fruits ripen into sticky, black, sweet-tasting pods. They are a source of nutritious fodder for grateful cattle – a fact confirmed by the crops of sturdy seedlings that emerge from the cowpats.

◆ FABACEAE *Pea and Bean family (Leguminosae)*

West Indian Ebony (*Brya ebenus*)

These small, shrubby trees have close-set, spiny-looking green leaflets and cracked brown bark on the main stems. They are natives of Jamaica and Cuba and grow naturally in dry, rocky places. *Brya ebenus* plants are deciduous and are only really noticeable when flowering. Then they develop an eye-catching display of fragrant, orange-yellow, pea-flowers that are thickly clustered along young, arching branches. The trees flower in cycles from spring to summer but are said to respond to rain (or to the rumours thereof) with more bloom. They produce a very hard, black, prized wood called ebony, which local people use to make carvings, pieces of household furniture and fence posts. Commercial ebony is a different product altogether and is obtained in Africa from the *Diospyros* trees of the Ebenaceae family.

Gungo Peas (*Cajanus cajan*)
Other name Pigeon peas

Cajanus cajan is an annual, branching shrub whose distinctive, grey-green foliage consists of trios of small, hairy leaflets. They are important food plants. Given favourable conditions, some can rapidly upgrade to the status of small trees. They are also highly seasonal plants that produce the main crop of peas at around Christmas time. Enterprising locals will sow Gungo Peas on any patch of soil deemed available – family plots, roadsides, hilltops and wasteland. Clusters of pretty, yellow-red, pea-flowers are borne in succession and these quickly develop into 3–4 in (8–10 cm) long pods. The very young peas are delicious eaten raw but most Jamaicans prefer them mature and cooked with rice. The plants are probably native to the East Indies. They can be grown at altitudes up to about 3000 ft (1000 m).

Donkey Fee-Fee (*Centrosema pubescens*)

The broad pea-flowers of *Centrosema pubescens* are carried on the slenderest of twining stems. Unless there is a convenient support nearby, the pretty, mauve-pink blossoms and triplet leaflets will remain at ground level. Usually, however, the plants are able to soar to the tops of high fences and climb into the lower branches of large trees. They are scattered thinly over a wide range of wayside habitats and altitudes. Although the main flowering season is from autumn to spring, there are always some plants in bloom at other times. Rural youngsters often collect the curved stamen tubes from the largest flowers. They remove and discard the contents then pop the empty tubes into their mouths. Sucking air into these tiny toys will produce high pitched, whistling noises. 'Fee-Fee' means a fife or whistle. These plants are natives of tropical America.

Blue Pea (*Clitoria ternatea*)
Other name Blue Vine

In the field, these attractive flowers are a startling, dark blue with yellow centres. They are borne by small, twining pea plants whose alternate, pinnate leaves have five to seven, light green leaflets. Blue Peas are native to the Old World tropics. They were originally garden plants here, but have long since escaped to grow wild where they can – which is from sea level up to altitudes of about 650 ft (200 m). They are perennials and bloom all year. White-flowered plants are rare.

Duppy Machete (*Erythrina corallodendrum*)
Other names Spanish Machete, Cutlass Bush

Duppy Machete trees are native to the Caribbean. They grow naturally in woodlands and thickets in areas up to 3 000 ft (1 000 m) high and have been widely planted as living fence posts. Although they can grow to 30 ft (10 m) tall, the trees usually achieve less than half that height, often appearing to be damaged and stunted. The bark is pale beige in colour and it becomes thick and ropey on some of the older trunks. The trees shed their triple, heart-shaped leaflets in early spring and at the same time begin to produce spikes of unusually shaped, crimson flowers. Each large, standard petal is folded along its length resembling a blood stained blade, 2–2 ½ins (5–6 cm) long and less than ½in (1 cm) wide. The short, brownish calyx, together with the remaining, reduced petals provide a creditable, ½in (1cm) long handle. In Jamaican folklore, these tiny, floral machetes are suitable for use in the spirit world.

Erythrina (*Erythrina variegata* var. *orientalis,* syn *E. parcelli*)

The variety *orientalis* is a widely-planted specimen tree, judged beautiful both for its foliage and flowers. First, there are the trios of heart-shaped leaflets that are strikingly variegated in yellow or pale green along the veins. Full-grown trees in sunlight can achieve a glowing aura that is complemented by their pale, white-grey bark. Then there are the dagger-shaped, eye-catching bright crimson blooms. Flowering, although sometimes sparse, is best in spring when the trees suffer some leaf loss. The trunks and larger branches carry substantial, curved, black-tipped thorns. The non-variegated form, 'Coral Tree', has plain leaves and grey bark attractively streaked in shades of green, pink and orange. Its dramatic orange-red blooms consist of the $2\frac{1}{2}$-3 ins (6–7 cm) long; semi-folded, standard petals and bunches of crimson stamens. The remaining petals are reduced to a quarter that length. The elongated, grey ovaries develop into knobbly pods that contain dark purple seeds. These and all other *Erythrina* seeds are reportedly poisonous. The trees are native to tropical Asia.

Immortelle (*Erythrina poeppigiana*)

Tall Immortelle trees flower unforgettably in spring. Their leafless crowns become a shimmer of orange visible from afar. The bloom is made up of a wealth of slanting flowering spikes, some 6–8 ins (16–20 cm) long that are thickly coated with buds and blossoms. On closer inspection, each open flower seems pink-tinged and consists mainly of two separated, curving parts – the standard and keel petals. The bundle of stamens and green, baby pod are sheathed for most of their length in the sickle-shaped keel. The trees have compound leaves each made up of three, large, diamond-shaped leaflets. Their whitish bark carries dark streaks and sizeable thorns that are concentrated near to the bases of the stems. Many fine Immortelles can be seen by the roadsides when travelling between Bog Walk and Mount Diablo. There are even more growing in the valley of the Wag Water River, especially around Castleton. This specimen was photographed near Irish Town in the hills of St. Andrew. Immortelles are natives of Peru and are now widespread in the West Indies and West Africa. The trees were often planted to provide shade for tender crops such as coffee and cocoa.

Grow Stick (*Gliricidia sepium*)
Other names Quick Stick, Aaron's Rod

Grow Sticks are fast-growing, tropical American trees, that are very easily propagated. As their local names imply, new plants will quickly develop from woody cuttings or sticks that are simply pushed into the ground. The trees are thickly covered with soft, green, pinnate foliage. Each compound leaf has eight pairs of pointed leaflets and a single terminal leaflet. Flowering occurs from December to April when many, young, arching branches lose their leaves. They then become clustered with attractive, pink, pea-flowers that have yellow centres. *Gliricidia sepium* is widely used for providing shade, hedging and as living fence posts from coastal pasturelands up to hill-top plots.

Millettia (*Millettia* spp.)

Millettias are small to medium-sized trees that are native to tropical West Africa. They carry dense tresses of dark green leaves and are frequently planted in car parks to provide shade. Each pinnate leaf consists of four, paired, shiny leaflets, which increase in size towards the single, largest, terminal leaflet. The trees bloom conspicuously in spring while renewing their leaves and sporadically throughout the remainder of the year. They produce beautiful, lavender, pea-type flowers with bright, creamy centres. There are about two dozen blooms and buds on each short, flowering stalk. These mature into flat pods that may be 6–9 ins (16–23 cm) long and are widest towards their free ends.

Millettia spp.

◆ ZYGOPHYLLACEAE

Lignum Vitae (*Guaiacum officinale*)

Lignum Vitae translates as 'Tree' or 'Wood of Life'. It is rather well known as it bears the National Flower of Jamaica and is also the National Tree of The Bahamas. Unusually, the most commonly used name is in Latin. *Lignum Vitae* is an elegant, rounded, evergreen tree, typically some 13–26 ft (4–8 m) high. It has mottled, patchwork bark and bears small, glossy leaflets. It is widely planted as a shade or specimen tree and often displays the endearing local habit of whitewashing (painting) the lower half of the tree trunk. The lavender-blue flowers are borne several times during the year and are sometimes seen together with the orange, heart-shaped fruits. These offerings prove irresistible to clouds of white butterflies, which can often be seen dancing with delight through the branches. The hard, bi-coloured wood is heavy and full of resin – it is so dense it will sink in water. It is therefore prized for making carvings, butcher's blocks, pulleys, cogs, etc and was formerly famous for providing ships' propellers and police batons. Extracts from the bark, sap and leaves were once used as medicines for diseases such as arthritis and syphilis. Small bunches of *Lignum Vitae* are still hung up on stalls and in shops and homes to deter flies. The tree is a native of tropical America and grows in abundance here in the southern coastal plains such as Kingston and Treasure Beach.

Kingston Buttercup (*Tribulus cistoides*)
Other names Bicycle Bur, Police Macca

Kingston Buttercups are common in tropical places. They grow island-wide and are quickly recognised by the bright yellow flowers that thrust up from a mass of light green, feathery foliage. The creeping, hairy stems with their pairs of pinnate leaves create patches on the roadsides and they also carpet more extensive, flat areas of sandy wasteland. One leaf of a pair is always bigger than the other. This larger leaf consists of about eight pairs of soft, oblong leaflets, twice that of its companion. All leaflets close after sundown. Flower stalks arise singly in the axils of the smaller leaf throughout the year. The flowers are bigger than buttercups and they are sometimes cream-coloured. These vivid blooms track the sun. Many small, round fruit are produced. They are only about $\frac{1}{2}$ in (1cm) in length but possess sizeable spines, which can cause serious discomfort to the bare-footed and may just possibly, damage the bicycle tyres of police constables!

◆ RUTACEAE

Lime Tree (*Citrus aurantifolia*)

These small, prickle-studded trees are popular members of the orange, grapefruit, tangerine and lemon clan. Lime trees are natives of tropical Asia and are raised here in virtually every Jamaican backyard. Lime leaves are stalked ovals which have finely jagged edges, pale undersides and when crushed give off a spicy fragrance. The trees continually produce small bunches of exquisite, citrus-scented flowers. Each has four, satiny-white, recurved petals, a handful of stamens and a prominent, orange-headed pistil. The fruit, limes, can reach the size of golf balls and they are used here in place of lemons. Lime juice is an essential ingredient of rum punch. The sweetened juice also makes the staple thirst quencher, limeade, also called 'bellywash'. Limes have a hundred and one other creative uses in local households.

China Box (*Murraya paniculata*)
Other name Mock Orange

China Box shrubs are thickly covered with small, shiny, dark green leaflets that have a tangy, refreshing scent when crushed. They make exceedingly popular hedge plants but can only flower freely when grown as specimen shrubs or small trees. Then, several times a year they become wreathed in bunches of white flowers. Each perfumed flower has four satiny, recurved petals and a prominent pistil like its Citrus relatives. Scent from the massed bloom can quickly become cloying to humans but remains irresistible to the insect world. The resulting fruit are attractive, red berries.

◆ MALPIGHIACEAE

Stigmaphyllon (*Stigmaphyllon emarginatum*)

The seasonal, eye-catching display of yellow blossom seen brightening thorn trees and sandy mounds along Palisadoes is *Stigmaphyllon emarginatum*. This indigenous vine starts life as a low-growing plant sporting many pairs of soft, hairy, grey-green leaves. Its twining stems soon scramble up into any available larger plant. The vines bloom best in autumn and spring when numerous small, densely-packed inflorescences crowd the plants. The buds blaze into dozens of bright flowers, each bearing five, stalked and crinkle-edged petals. Although the vines are found most frequently by the sea, they also flourish inland up to about 3 000 ft (900 m).

◆ EUPHORBIACEAE *Cassava family*

Cat Tail (*Acalypha hispida*)
Other name Chenille Plant

Cat Tails are fast-growing, soft-stemmed plants from tropical Asia. They provide a leafy backdrop in gardens but are really cultivated for their astonishing, rope-like, crimson inflorescences. These hanging spikes are composed of a forest of sticky stamens protruding from hundreds of tiny flowers. The long-lasting spikes may each exceed 12 ins (30 cm) in length and together with the wide, pointed leaves are arranged alternately along the stems.

Crown-of-Thorns (*Euphorbia milii,* syn. *E. splendens*)

This prickly, scrambling, Madagascan shrub normally grows to about 3 ft (90 cm) tall. The plants have short, thorn-covered, woody stems, thin, elongated leaves and they bear clusters of tiny, lipstick-bright flowers. The petals of these 'kissy' red or pink blooms are really enlarged bracts. *Euphorbia milii* plants will grow in full sunshine and tolerate drought, but like other family members, their stems contain a white, irritant sap.

Poinsettia (*Euphorbia pulcherrima*)
Other name Christmas Bush

For most of the year Poinsettias are ordinary shrubs with medium-sized, scalloped leaves and inconspicuous, yellow and red flowers. Towards late autumn and Christmas time, the shorter daylight hours stimulate groups of leaves (bracts), surrounding the flowers to blush bright red! The plants then become exceedingly noticeable and popular. They are now familiar in temperate regions as smaller, potted versions and are available in many different hues – pinks, yellows and white! Poinsettias need planned pruning to prevent them becoming awkward, spindly trees but beware of the thick, white, irritant sap.

Coral Plant (*Jatropha integerrima*)

Jatropha integerrima shrubs are native to Cuba and Puerto Rico. Here they are garden plants growing to a little over 9 ft (3 m) tall. They have an open framework of slender, grey-barked stems, which become attractively streaked in black as they age. Their light-green leaves are pointed, alternate and are borne on relatively long stalks. These Jatrophas flower freely – the plants are often laden with bunches of coral-coloured blooms. Each pretty, 1 in (3 cm) wide flower has five, bright, crimson petals and a stalked cluster of orange-red stamens. A few, small, three-lobed fruit are produced.

Bottle Plant (*Jatropha podagrica*)
Other names Coral Plant, Gouty Foot

Jatropha podagrica shrubs originated in Central America. They are garden ornamentals visually similar to the closely-related Castor Oil and Cassava They are a hardy lot, cultivated for their coral-red or orange flowers and striking, large, lobed leaves. The shrubs can grow more than 5 ft (1.5 m) tall with succulent stems that are characteristically swollen or bottle-shaped towards the base. Bottle Plant sap will irritate the skin and its seeds are poisonous to humans – however, birds love them. *Jatropha multifida* is similar in flower but lacks the swollen stem base and has deeply-cut leaves that carry up to eleven, finger-like, pointed lobes.

Jatropha podagrica

Castor Oil (*Ricinus communis*)
Other name Oil Nut

Castor Oil shrubs are African plants. They are now universal in Jamaica as part crop, part weed. They are handsome, hardy and very fast-growing – many achieve temporary tree status. The plants are cultivated for their oil-rich seeds and the shade provided by their large, deeply lobed leaves. They flower continuously, bearing the small, yellow, male flowers towards the base of the inflorescence. The larger, female flowers each have three, two-part, red stigmas which persist well into maturation. These flowers develop into dozens of three-lobed capsules or nuts. The oil is easily expressed from the big seeds within and it is used in local medicine as a strong purgative and in cosmetic (hair) preparations. There is a long list of other applications. The plants vary enormously, some have red fruit and purplish leaves but all are poisonous and are shunned by livestock.

◆ MALVACEAE

Blue Mahoe (*Hibiscus elatus*)
Other names Mountain Mahoe, Cuba Bark

Blue Mahoes are Jamaica's beautiful, National Trees. These elegant trees are widely planted for timber and also double as shade-giving ornamentals. They have large, rough-textured, heart-shaped leaves and straight trunks that can grow 65–85 ft (20–25 m) tall. Flowering is best in spring, when a succession of big, but short-lived, Hibiscus-type blooms is produced. The decorative flowers emerge bearing yellow or orange petals. However, they soon darken to crimson or bronze, fade and fall within a day or so. The hard, grey-brown wood contains attractive blonde streaks. It is highly prized for its colouring and durability. The wood is used mainly for making carvings and furniture. Blue Mahoe trees are native to both Cuba and Jamaica.

Okra (*Hibiscus esculentus,* syn. *Abelmoschus esculentus*)
Other names Gumbo, Ladies Fingers

Okras themselves are small, green vegetables that grow stiffly on hairy shrubs. The plants, which originated in the Old World tropics, are widely cultivated here. They are about 5 ft (1.5 m) tall at maturity and bear large, lobed leaves with toothed margins. The big, yellow flowers have dark red, internal bases and quickly develop into short, upright and succulent pods. These are produced throughout the year. When boiled, the many-seeded pods or 'fingers' become soft and slimy – you either love or hate them.

Hibiscus (*Hibiscus rosa-sinensis*)
Other names China Rose, Shoe Black

Hibiscus flowers are the delightful hallmarks of hot, tropical places. This is one of the originals remembered by school children of yesteryear, who would crumble the exotic blossoms to a darkening liquid, which they then used to clean their writing slates and shine their black shoes. The plants have enormous popularity and appeal matched by an explosive development of dozens of different types. Leaves are generally oval in shape with scalloped edges. The flowers can be single, double or triple, match most rainbow shades or even be bi-coloured. However, there is a common, underlying theme. The flowers are large and widely-opened, with petals curved back to some degree. Both stamens and stigmas are carried on one slender, central tube which hangs well clear of the petals. The beautiful blooms are short-lived, lasting just one day. Long-beaked hummingbirds sip nectar directly from the open corolla, but they and other birds with shorter beaks often punch holes at the bases of the flowers to obtain the same reward. The plants originated in Asia.

Sorrel (*Hibiscus sabdariffa*)
Other name Roselle

Hibiscus sabdariffa is a widely-cultivated, seasonal annual that grows to about 5 ft (1.5 m) tall. It is native to the Old World tropics. Sorrel leaves range from being simple to having three or five lobes. In autumn, the plants begin to bear attractive, light pink or yellow flowers, each with a prominent, dark red smudge at the base of the petals. As the fruits (capsules) mature, their rings of sepals (calyces) lengthen to between $1\frac{1}{4}$ and $1\frac{1}{2}$ ins (3 and 3.5 cm), swell and change dramatically from green to bright red or purple. These are picked and used to brew the popular, red, astringent drink of the same name essential for the Jamaican Christmas celebrations. A variety, which has larger, white calyces, has been developed.

Coral Hibiscus (*Hibiscus schizopetalus*)

This plant seems to be a rather more elegant, African offshoot of *Hibiscus rosa-sinensis*. The feathery-looking blooms of *H. schizopetalus* hang by long stalks from the tips of arching branches. The flowers, which here are either pink or red, have deeply-cut, wavy petals so completely turned back on themselves that they point upwards, revealing the entire length of the hooked, stamen tube.

Hibiscus schizopetalus

Tree Cotton (*Gossypium barbadense*)

At a distance, these perennial, cotton plants appear as loosely-branched shrubs made untidy by hanging twists of a whitish material and bits and bobs of dead, brown twig. Closer inspection reveals small, green, flower buds each enclosed by an inner, cup-like calyx and three, broad, outer bracts which sport an average of six, pointed, piratical-looking teeth. The hand-sized leaves are alternate and they vary between being plain, heart-shaped or having three to five lobes. The attractive flowers, like many other family members, change colour over their short lives. Each new bloom has pale yellow petals with maroon spots at their bases. By the day's end, yellow has darkened to a purplish-pink and the faded flowers have shut. Tree cotton fruits are small capsules that split apart when dry – exposing the familiar, downy, white fibres. This wild cotton used to be gathered for stuffing soft toys and cushions. Cotton was once cultivated commercially in Jamaica and many specimens growing wild today are the results of natural hybridisation between indigenous and introduced varieties.

Pepper Hibiscus (*Malvaviscus arboreus* var. *penduliflorus*)
Other names Sleeping Hibiscus, Turk's Cap, Turk's Hat

The closed, red, pink or white blossoms of Pepper Hibiscus always hang from their branches. Although the folded petals never open, the flowers give every appearance of being Hibiscus at heart. Indeed, they were originally named *Hibiscus malvaviscus* and this is remembered in some of the common names. The hairy leaves of these 5 ft (1.5 m) tall shrubs may be lance-shaped or lobed in outline. They originated in Central America and have become almost as popular here as their open flowered relatives. Pepper Hibiscus plants grow and flower in great abundance in the hilly districts for most of the year. The wild form, *Malvaviscus arboreus*, has short, furled, red petals and these blooms do not necessarily point downwards. They are known collectively as 'Suck-Bush' – a graphic description of how children extract the droplets of nectar from the flowers after removing the petals.

Malvaviscus arboreus

Seaside Mahoe (*Thespesia populnea*)

These scrambling, coastal shrubs or trees can grow right down to the water's edge, mingling there with the mangrove species. Both kinds of plant seem able to exist on almost bare limestone rock and must endure the salt spray. The mahoes are thickly covered with leathery, heart-shaped leaves and they bear a succession of beautiful, short-lived blooms. Their lemon-yellow petals, which have red smudges at their bases, overlap to form large, well-opened corollas. The flowers quickly darken to orange-purple and close within a day. The persistent fruits are rounded capsules that are characteristically flattened at their free ends. Seaside Mahoes are widespread tropical plants.

◆ BEGONIACEAE

Wild Begonia (*Begonia minor*)
Other name Rock Rose

Wild Begonia plants appear as soon you start the climb up to the mountains – particularly those above and around Kingston. These slender, succulent stems arch from the crumbly hillsides carrying fleshy, pink-flushed inflorescences. There are also white and red flowered varieties. Male flowers have two big and two small petals while the female counterparts, with obvious, three-sided ovaries, have full heads of uniform petals. The pointed leaves are large, lopsided and arranged alternately along the branches. *Begonia minor* is one of three endemic out of about nine, wild species. There are also many other garden and 'escaped' Begonias found throughout the island.

◆ CUCURBITACEAE *Cucumber and Squash family*

Cerasee (*Momordica charantia*)

Cerasee (pronounced 'Surcey') is an attractive, yellow-flowered, rampant vine. Using coiling tendrils, the plants scramble through bushes, clothe waste ground and hide fences in drapes of bright green. The young stems and artistically lobed, five-part leaves give off an acrid odour when bruised. This local 'mile-a-minute' is the most popular of legal herbs and many Jamaicans drink the intensely bitter bush tea as a preventative or cure for a host of ailments. The leaves can be easily soaked and pulped in water and the resultant extract used as a face and body wash. There is also a widespread belief that Cerasee baths are effective against feared skin disorders. The vines bear a succession of small, green, textured fruits, which ripen to orange-red then split to reveal the red seeds that are beloved by birds but poisonous to humans. *Momordica charantia* plants are found throughout the tropics and subtropics.

◆ LYTHRACEAE

June Rose (*Lagerstroemia indica*)

June Roses are grown as many-stemmed, 5 ft (1.5 m) tall shrubs in gardens and as massed plantings in parks. Their foliage consists of slightly staggered (subopposite) pairs of oval leaves arranged on young, squared stems. Pea-sized, smooth-skinned buds develop at the tips of branches and they open to form close-packed, conical heads of attractive, crinkly blooms. The flowers range in colour from white through the pinks and reds to mauve. They are at their glowing best at mid-year, as the name suggests, but the plants have a long-lasting flowering season. The blooms can often be so weighty as to bow their branches toward the ground. These ornamental favourites originated in South-east Asia and Northern Australia.

Queen of Flowers (*Lagerstroemia speciosa*)
Other names Crape or Crepe Myrtle, June Rose

Queen of Flowers is the tree-sized version of the June Rose shrub, *Lagerstroemia indica*. These trees, which can attain a towering 46 ft (14 m) in height, were once plentiful along the roadsides. Several remain in Hope Gardens. There is a small stand of trees at the Lacovia end of Bamboo Avenue in St. Elizabeth as well as alongside parts of the Norman Manley Boulevard, which runs through Negril. Together with those in other parks and gardens, these trees still provide the legendary bloom from late spring through summer when inflorescences, which may be 2 ft (60 cm) or more in length, emerge from the tips of the dark-leaved branches. Their big, ribbed buds burst into pink or purple, fan-shaped flowers. White blossoms are rare. Each flower consists of five, crimped, crinkled and stalked petals and, en masse, they outline the trees in a long-lasting fiesta of flowering. *Lagerstroemia speciosa* is native to South-east Asia.

Pomegranate (*Punica granatum*)

These hardy, spare-looking shrubs are commonly planted as hedging or as specimen fruit trees. They have been known since antiquity in southern Europe and grow here in Jamaica to between 6 and 10 ft (2 and 3 m) tall. Their brittle, woody branches carry paired, papery, oblong leaves. The trees bloom modestly at intervals throughout the year when small groups of flowers are borne at the tips of a few branches. Pomegranate flowers are an attractive, fleshy, orange-red cast in an open, bell shape. These mature into the familiar, many seeded, round fruit, which often bear the remnants of the flower calyces.

◆ COMBRETACEAE

Rangoon Creeper (*Quisqualis indica*)
Other name Rice and Peas

This elegant, creeping vine comes from South-east Asia. The woody stems bear slightly staggered, paired leaves and hanging heads of tubular flowers. Their delicate, $2\frac{1}{2}$ in (6 cm) long blooms emerge white but soon darken to pink then red – colours which are reminiscent of one of our national dishes, rice and peas (red beans). Rangoon Creepers are commonly grown on fences, porches and other structures close to buildings for three reasons: the plants need support; they bloom throughout the year and the pleasing floral fragrance is particularly good at night.

Bottle Brush Tree (*Callistemon lanceolatus*)

These popular, municipal plants are kept to shrub size along principal roads, but they can grow up to 10 ft (3 m) tall. Bottle Brush trees originate in Australia but only this red-flowered form is common here. They bear a multitude of slender, weeping branches, which are covered in short, aromatic, spear-shaped leaves. Each inflorescence consists of dozens of small, brightly-coloured tufts arranged in rows like the bristles of a bottlebrush. They are in fact the stamens of the much smaller flowers. The branches go through several episodes of flowering and growth as shown by the succession of small, hard, cup-like fruits left behind.

◆ **ONAGRACEAE** *Evening Primrose and Fuchsia family*

Ludwigia (*Ludwigia octovalvis*)

This *Ludwigia* is a bushy, small-leaved shrub that is always firmly rooted in or near to ponds, ditches, swamps, streams and other sources of fresh water. The plants grow up to 4 ft (120 cm) tall and bear many pointed leaves on their reddish, woody branches. *Ludwigia* shrubs produce a dazzle of bright yellow blossoms many times a year. The flowers are up to $1\frac{1}{2}$ ins (3.5 cm) wide and grow singly in the axils of the leaves. Each has four petals, four green sepals and behind these a long, narrow ovary. The resulting fruit is a distinctive, ribbed capsule up to 2 ins (5 cm) long, which is usually capped by the persistent calyx. *Ludwigia octovalvis* is a common tropical and subtropical plant. Jamaica also hosts ten other members of this moisture-loving genus.

♦ **ARALIACEAE** *Ivy family*

Umbrella Tree (*Schefflera actinophylla*)

Schefflera actinophylla makes large, leafy pot plants commonly sold in units of three per container. These can rapidly outgrow their situation and then are often planted outdoors in the garden. They make unusual looking trios of slender trees with drooping foliage. Single specimens are, of course, planted in parks and other gardens. Each long leaf stalk terminates in a circle of large, downward pointing leaflets, like an umbrella. These trees are largely unbranched and flower when they grow to between 10 and 15 ft (3 – 5 m) tall. They then produce striking, many-spoked inflorescences from their topmost branches. The colourful radials may be up to 3 ft (1 m) long and they are studded on both sides by knots of small, hard, purplish flowers. These trees are natives of Australia and they flower here periodically throughout the year. *Schefflera sciadophyllum* is an endemic species common in the central and eastern hills. It has less showy, hanging flowering spikes that bear tiny stalked clusters of green buds and pinkish flowers.

Schefflera actinophylla

Blue Plumbago (*Plumbago auriculata*)

Leggy, hardy and fast growing, *Plumbago auriculata* is familiar as low hedging and specimen shrubs. The plants are always in bloom in shades of blue and white. Each delicate flower has a slender corolla tube which expands into five, wafer-thin petals. The flowers do not last long indoors. The young growth has a characteristic hairy and sticky feel. The alternative name of *P. capensis* is a reminder of Capetown Province, one of their places of origin in South Africa. The wild form, *P. scandens*, called 'Burr Vine' has sparse, white flowers. These plants are widespread and their starry blooms peek out from hedges, roadsides, thickets and undergrowth.

Plumbago auriculata

◆ GENTIANACAEAE

Jamaican Fuchsia (*Lisianthius longifolius*)

There are eight, similar endemic species of *Lisianthius* that prefer growing in upland areas. *Lisianthius longifolius* is common on roadside banks and in thickets at altitudes up to about 5600 ft (1700 m). These perennial, yellow-flowered plants are slender, branched creations, which often project perilously from steep hillsides. They have paired, elliptical leaves and the plants repeatedly produce many sprays of attractive, tubular blooms. The flowers spring from toothed, ribbed calyces and terminate in a stellar arrangement of five, pointed petals. The slender, hanging blossoms can reach $2\frac{1}{2}$ ins (6.5 cm) in length. Their yellow stamens and greenish-tipped stigma are clearly visible. These appealing plants are apparently unnoticed by local gardeners.

◆ **APOCYNACEAE** *Oleander family*

Allamanda (*Allamanda cathartica*)
Other name Yellow Allamanda

Big, bright and beautiful are the golden trumpet flowers of *Allamanda cathartica*, which, together with the whorls of long, glossy leaves, make the plant easy to recognise. Allamandas are widely grown as shrubs, hedging or vines. The plants are natives of Brazil and are considered to be totally toxic. They flower all year round but the blooms seem particularly abundant and vivid in the hot, dry summer. There are a handful of yellow garden varieties that differ mainly in the size of flower and the addition of red-brown colouring to the blooms. Some bear round, spiny fruit. The large flowered Chocolate Allamanda (*A. bletchii*) has a dark throat and bleached-brown petals. Purple Allamanda (*A. violacea*) has huge rose-pink blooms. Both are less common than Yellow Allamanda.

Allamanda cathartica

Ramgoat Roses (*Catharanthus roseus*)
Other names Old Maids, Periwinkle, Vinca

This is a very common, low-growing, almost weed-like plant of gardens, roadsides and wasteland areas. The plants are in flower for most of the year and reliably brighten their environs with their pretty blooms and shiny, dark leaves. They come from Madagascar and thrive in dry, low-level locations. The flat, five-petalled flowers come in shades of pink, red and white. Some have darker or contrasting throats. These homely blooms are not cut flower favourites as they tend to develop unpleasant odours when imprisoned in vases. There is continuing pharmaceutical interest in the use of periwinkle plant extracts for the treatment of cancers and other ailments. Unusually, the ever-present herds of hungry goats ignore these plants.

Deadly Nightshade (*Echites umbellata*)

This Deadly Nightshade is common in coastal, limestone areas. The attractive plants grow prostrate in cleared areas as well as being caught up into thickets and are best seen snaking through rough grass. They have paired, elongated leaves and bear clusters of vivid, white bloom nearly all year. Each open flower has five, wavy-edged petals that unite to form a charmingly twisted, tubular base. Some develop into thick-walled fruit called follicles that range from 3–9 ins (9–26 cm) in length. *Echites umbellata* plants are found in tropical America and the West Indies. They are poisonous to people and large, grazing animals.

Oleander (*Nerium oleander*)

The original pink, fragrant Oleanders came from the Mediterranean. Today, the plants grow and flower across the island. The blooms are available in many different colours and in either single or double form. Oleanders make leggy shrubs that bear narrow, pointy leaves. The plants can grow to tree size if not discouraged. They are, above all, extremely hardy and will produce the common, bright, pink, red or white flowers all year round under almost all conditions. Less appealing dwarf forms exist. The irritant milky sap and all other plant parts are known to be poisonous.

Frangipani (*Plumeria rubra*)

Plumeria rubra plants can bear yellow, white or rose-coloured flowers. The blooms on this cultivated variant have creamy-white petals with buttery-yellow centres. They grow on small to medium-sized, fleshy shrubs or trees that are prized for their long lasting and sweetly scented blossoms. Frangipani flowers develop in packed clusters that are all borne at the crowns of the trees. The broad, elliptical leaves may be up to 16 ins (40 cm) long and they possess characteristic, connecting veins along the margins. The leaves are shed completely at least once a year exposing the elegant network of rather chubby, bare branches. Infestation by the impressive, yellow-banded, black caterpillars of a common hawk moth also causes defoliation. The wild, evergreen *P. obtusa* plants bear similar, white, yellow-centred flowers. These and the many other *Plumeria* species are native to tropical America and the West Indies.

Plumeria rubra

Tabernaemontana divaricata

Coffee Rose (*Tabernaemontana divaricata*)

Coffee Rose shrubs are popular, old-fashioned plants that bear fragrant, double-flowered blooms. There is a marked resemblance to Gardenia plants which are members of the Rubiaceae family. The rounded Coffee Rose shrubs are well covered with perky, glossy, green leaves that have deep set and visible veins. Dotted in and about the foliage are clusters of rose-like flowers and their elegant, pointed buds. The tubular blooms have several pure white petals delicately folded around each other. This variety has a sweet, fleeting scent and their flowers last well in vases. The single-flowered form, *T. corymbosa*, has five blade-like petals arranged propeller fashion. It makes a very decorative, white-starred shrub that is frequently planted as low hedging in public places.

Lucky Nut/Seed (*Thevetia peruviana*)

Lucky Seeds are small, refined-looking trees from tropical America now found thinly scattered all over the island. They have been planted at the roadsides, in gardens and parks and can be seen thriving as wild plants. These appealing ornamentals have crooked branches and shiny, narrow-leaved foliage, which is decorated with small clusters of bell-shaped flowers. The blooms may be salmon-pink or plain yellow and are produced all year round. The double-sided nut (seed) is rumoured to bring good luck in financial matters. Newcomers are advised to store a specimen in their wallets – the money should double sometime soon! On the other hand, it should also be noted that the entire plant is described as being very poisonous because of its milky sap or latex.

Nightsage (*Urechites lutea*, syn. *Pentalinon luteum*)
Other names Deadly Nightshade, Wild Allamanda

Urechites lutea shrubs possess instant appeal due to their slender, twining stems, shiny foliage and flaring, yellow blooms. They are widespread in the Caribbean and Florida where they flower and fruit all year. This is one of the most visible of several plants known as Deadly Nightshade in Jamaica. They are common country plants forming clumps in fields or scrambling up fences, hedges, utility poles or neighbouring shrubs. Although they closely resemble the cultivated Allamandas, *Urechites lutea* plants seem more delicate and their leaves are borne in pairs and not in whorls. They also regularly produce long, twin, pod-like capsules that can reach 8 ins (20 cm) in length. Like many other family members these viney shrubs are rated toxic to humans and farm animals.

◆ ASCLEPIADACEAE *Milkweed family*

Red Head (*Asclepias curassavica*)
Other names Butterfly Weed, Blood Flower

Brightly-flowered Red Head weeds appear at roadsides and in a variety of other waste places. They can grow up to 3 ft (1 m) tall but are usually shorter, rather solitary plants that bear pairs of smooth, lance-shaped leaves and small heads of glowing, bi-coloured blooms all year. Each tiny flower has five, orange-red petals and an additional inner ring of yellow, petal-like units and stamens. The upright, spindle-shaped fruits occur in small groups. Although the plants are well supplied with milky, poisonous sap, they play an important role in traditional herbal medicine. Children are taught early on to recognise Red Head plants and to distinguish them from the similar but relatively inoffensive Wild Sages (*Lantana* spp.). These and other milkweeds are important to birds and insects. Milkweed flowers provide nectar and their leaves are food for the caterpillars (larvae) of the Monarch butterfly. *Asclepias curassavica* plants are natives of tropical South America. They have now spread to the rest of the continent and other tropical and subtropical areas throughout the world.

Duppy Cho-Cho (*Calotropis procera*)
Other names Duppy Cotton, French Cotton, Giant Milkweed

These fleshy-looking, 6 ft (2 m) tall shrubs grow freely in rough, dry, coastal areas. Some go on to tree size. The plants have an architectural, eye-catching quality that is enhanced by the bluish-grey sheen of the young growth. Each plant may have many, pale-coloured stems which carry, large, light green leaves, and clusters of stiff, attractive, blossoms. The white, purple-tipped, velvety flowers are produced all year. A few mature into soft, green, sac-like fruits, which resemble cho-chos (*Sechium edule*) a popular local vegetable. Eventually, the fruits split and release drifts of small, brown seeds each equipped with a silky parachute. *Calotropis procera* plants are native to Africa and Asia where the poisonous white sap is an ingredient in folk medicines. I have found Monarch butterfly caterpillars (larvae) munching away at the leathery leaves and followed their transformation to pupae and adults. Jamaican children used to be warned not to stand under or too close to Duppy Cho-Cho plants at night as they ran the risk of being boxed (slapped) in the face by the resident Duppy! If this happened, their faces would remain forever twisted by the blow!

Purple Allamanda (*Cryptostegia madagascariensis*)
Other name Rubber Vine

These attractive, twining shrubs are commonplace in local gardens and roadside thickets on the north coast. They are characterised by their gleaming, dark green leaves, slender, pointed buds, and lovely purple pink, bell-shaped flowers. The mature fruit is a surprisingly large, ridged, woody capsule. Inside there is a smooth, cinnamon-coloured spindle containing dozens of small, parachute equipped seeds. The shrubs are understandably, but confusingly, known as Purple Allamanda. However, they are not related to the true Allamandas of the Apocynaceae family. The fruit, paired leaves and overflowing latex of *Cryptostegia madagascariensis* are distinctive. Be careful of the abundant, white juice or latex present in the stems. It can temporarily numb, irritate and stain your fingers. Elsewhere, however, the latex is an important, commercial source of rubber. *Cryptostegia grandiflora* (Indian Rubber Vine) differs mainly in the size and colour of its blooms. The flowers are clearly larger and very pale. They are streaked purple-pink on the outside but are entirely white inside. These vines are abundant on the south-east coast near Bull Bay. *Cryptostegia madagascariensis*, as the name suggests, comes from Madagascar.

Cryptostegia madagascariensis

◆ CONVOLVULACEAE

Morning Glory (*Ipomoea fistulosa*)

Unlike the host of vine-like Ipomoeas this Morning Glory is a spreading shrub that grows 6–10 ft (2–3 m) tall. They are common garden items flowering in cycles throughout the year. The plants bear heart-shaped leaves and large numbers of big, mauve-pink, trumpet-shaped blooms. Their delicate, tissue-thin corollas are short lived. They close soon after midday in response to daytime heat. Morning Glory plants are from tropical America.

Christmas Pops (*Turbina corymbosa*)

Christmas Pops grow on vine-like plants. Unsurprisingly, these vines flower abundantly around the festive season. Their fragrant blooms are best seen in the mists and dews of early morning, well before the flowers close at noon. The twining stems bear beautiful, wreath-like clusters of white, bell-shaped flowers that are set about with soft, heart-shaped leaves. Each flower has a dark red base to its throat and five, light green segments which alternate with the fused, white petals of the corolla. The plants are common in the West Indies and in tropical America. Here in Jamaica they grow in hilly, limestone districts such as those above Montego Bay.

◆ BORAGINACEAE

Duppy Cherry (*Cordia dentata*, syn. *C. alba*)
Other name White Cordia

White Cordia shrubs are well known in the West Indies and tropical America. They are commonplace here on some coastal plains and not infrequently grow into 35 ft (10 m) tall trees. Their oval, alternate leaves are hairy and finely scalloped in outline. The plants flower several times a year, when the sloping branches can become laden with flattened heads of creamy, yellow-tinged blossom. The lace-like inflorescences look very attractive against the dark green foliage. They consist of clusters of cup-shaped flowers whose fused petals have wavy rims. These small, fragrant blooms are much appreciated by the butterfly population. The resulting small, oblong fruit are called Duppy cherries – possibly because they become ghostly white and translucent when ripe. *Cordia collococca* is very similar but bears a profusion of barely edible, red berries called Clammy cherries.

Cordia dentata

Cordia sebestena flowers and fruit (inset)

Red Cordia (*Cordia sebestena*)
Other names Anaconda, Cordium, Geranium Tree, Geiger Tree, Scarlet Cordia, Spanish Cordia

Red Cordias are small, shapely trees that are rich in names and good looks. They are indigenous to the coastal, scrub areas of West Indian islands and are regularly planted here in Jamaica as roadside ornamentals. Their dark green, hand-sized leaves have the texture of sandpaper and they contrast beautifully with both its clusters of bright red or orange, tubular flowers and bunches of white, edible fruit. The flowering heads superficially resemble those of garden geraniums (*Pelargonium* spp.). *Cordia* trees flower and fruit throughout the year.

◆ VERBENACEAE

Bleeding Heart Vine (*Clerodendrum thomsoniae*)

These shrubs are West African in origin. They have weak, woody stems that climb and twine their way up trees, hedges, fences and other supports. Both foliage and flower heads appear to be rather stiff and prone to rustle when touched. The paired, oval leaves are dark green. These perennial plants produce flattened, fan-like inflorescences all year round. Their delicate, tubular, red flowers have five, free petals and a waft of protruding stamens. The name 'Bleeding Heart' was probably suggested by the appearance of the persistent, bud-shaped calyces. Each consists of five, fused and purplish sepals, which are attractive in their own right. *Clerodendrum thomsoniae* is sometimes called 'Rice and Peas' (a reference to the national dish of rice and red beans) but this name more fittingly belongs to the red-flowered variety that has white sepals.

Angel's Whisper (*Duranta repens*)
Other names Golden Tears, Poison Macca

Despite the trio of worrying names, these elegant ornamentals are grown in parks, hotel gardens and in the grounds of other establishments. They also grow wild up to about 5 500 ft (1 665 m). In cultivation, the thornless plants are usually kept at shrub size, however, they can grow to 20 ft (6 m) tall. They have paired, oval leaves whose edges become serrated from midline to tip. The shrubs are often at their prettiest when trailing from rocky footholds in the hills, their branches tipped for most of the year with an attractive scattering of starry, lavender blossoms. The honey-scented inflorescences are attended by swarms of insects. Each small, tubular flower has five, free petals. Two of these invariably carry a dark, central stripe. The strings of succulent, teardrop, orange berries look tempting but should not be eaten because they are poisonous. These plants are common throughout the tropical Americas and the West Indies.

Chinese Hat (*Holmskioldia sanguinea*)
Other name Japanese Hat

These tall garden shrubs have many arching, woody and 'whippy' branches. They are natives of India. Both the paired leaves and the short, paired inflorescences branch off together at intervals along the stems. The leaves, which may reach 4 ins (10 cm) in length, are more or less triangular with pronounced tips. Each is well veined but soft and the edges are serrated. Chinese Hats bloom all year round. The blossom is strung out along the branches and often tightly clustered at the tips. Their flowers are unusual – each small, lipped corolla tube is bent and rises from the centre of a circular, hat-like calyx. Orange-flowered plants are more commonly found, but other varieties bearing red, yellow-green and purplish flowers also exist. The tubular petals are short-lived, but the papery 'hats', which may be $1\frac{1}{2}$ ins (3 cm) or so wide make particularly long-lasting cut flowers.

Orange Sage (*Lantana camara*)

One of many common Lantanas or Wild Sages, this decorative member grows in wasteland areas all over Jamaica. The hairy shrubs are usually less than 3 ft (1 m) tall but they can scramble or climb to greater heights. They have square stems and paired leaves with serrated edges. If the leaves are crushed they give off a pleasant, mint-like scent. Lantanas bloom all year producing small, tightly-packed heads of pretty, orange-red flowers. Most then mature to form bunches of attractive, blue-black berries. Youngsters have always delighted in picking and hurling these poisonous playthings at each other. Lantanas are natives of South America and West Africa, but several garden varieties are now available.

Queen's Wreath (*Petrea volubilis*)

Petrea volubilis is a vigorous, tropical American climbing shrub that can develop substantial mounds or drifts of stiff, hairy vegetation. The paired leaves are pointed, smooth-edged and are rough to the touch. Flowering occurs several times a year during which the plants produce numerous sprays of attractive, starry blossom. The five part 'flowers' are in fact persistent sepals that surround the inconspicuous, short-lived corollas. Most of these ornamental plants flower beautifully in shades of lavender or blue – white is uncommon.

◆ LAMIACEAE (LABIATAE)

Red Salvia (*Salvia coccinea*)
Other name Scarlet Sage

Red Salvias are erect plants that usually grow less than 18 ins (0.5 m) tall. They are particularly common strung out along the roadsides in the foothills of the Blue Mountains. The small, square stems are visibly hairy. Their paired, triangular leaves feel felty, have scalloped edges and will produce scent with a hint of mint when bruised. Terminal flower spikes carry whorls of familiar, tubular blooms. Each scarlet flower has a broad, lobed, lower lip and a bunch of protruding, pink-stemmed stamens and style. These Salvias transplant easily to the garden where each will branch and flower to satisfaction. *Salvia coccinea* is also found throughout tropical and subtropical America.

◆ SOLANACEAE   *Potato and Tomato family*

Brunfelsia (*Brunfelsia jamaicensis*)

This glossy-leaved plant is one of six endemic species of *Brunfelsia*. It has been planted in a few gardens and also grows wild in high altitude woodlands. The plants make interesting, scented shrubs about 3–6 ft (1–2 m) tall with dark green foliage and many clusters of creamy, yellow-tinged blooms. Each flower has a long, curving corolla tube and a head of four wide and rounded petals. *Brunfelsia jamaicensis* shrubs flower repeatedly throughout the year.

Angel's Trumpet (*Datura candida*, syn. *Brugmansia candida*)

Daturas belong to a genus of attractive though poisonous plants that came originally from tropical South America. This example is a widely-cultivated ornamental seen most frequently in hill gardens but also occasionally in the wild. The shrubs or small trees usually bear a full flush of large, trumpet-shaped flowers that hang from the branches. These impressive, pure white corollas frequently reach 1 ft (30 cm) in length and they are produced on and off all year. The corollas in other common varieties are tinged with cream, pink, orange or violet and they have a strong fragrance at night. Datura's complementary leaves are big, alternate and felty. *Datura stramonium* is the noxious 'Jimson Weed' or 'Devil's Trumpet'.

Datura candida

Chalice vine (*Solandra grandiflora*)

During late winter and spring tall mountain trees sport these dramatic, hanging blooms which are clearly not their own. The flowers belong to the indigenous Chalice Vine which has thick, woody stems that can climb to 35 ft (10 m). They bear dark green, leathery leaves that are close-packed on to the short, flowering branches. Each enormous, creamy-white bloom can be up to 10 ins (25 cm) long and is shaped like a flagon with an elongated, wineglass stem. The tubular calyx encloses this stem, which can be almost half the entire length of the flower. The cup-like portion has five, free lobes at its rim and five, purple nectar-guide lines that disappear into the greenish interior. This Chalice Vine bears red-fleshed, oval fruits that may measure 2 by 2 ins (5 by 5 cm). *Solandra hirsuta*, the very similar, all hairy, endemic species has white-fleshed berries. Garden varieties like the yellow-flowered *S. guttata*, 'Cup of Gold', bloom several times per year. These plants are toxic.

Solandra grandiflora

Potato Tree (*Solanum macranthum*)

'Unexpected' well describes this beautiful, Brazilian, ornamental tree as most family members are shrubs or climbers. These prickly trees grow to about 16 ft (5 m) tall and have large, lobed and hairy leaves. Most of the young growth is also hairy. Potato trees are always well supplied with clusters of big, multi-coloured flowers. Inflorescences regularly branch from the younger limbs. Each bud opens into a familiar but giant, tomato or (Irish) potato-type flower. The deep violet blooms are up to 3 ins (7 cm) wide and carry a clutch of yellow, contrasting stamens. These flowers are like chunky, five-part stars with darker lines radiating to the tips of the petals. The blooms fade from violet through shades of purple-pink to white. Some mature into round, orange-coloured fruit, which are the size of an average plum tomato.

Susumber (*Solanum torvum*)

These are common, sprawling, tropical shrubs that grow by the roadsides and in waste places up to an elevation of around 4000 ft (1200 m). They are usually less than 10ft (3 m) tall and have broad, hairy, matt-green leaves that carry a few prickles like the rest of the plant. The shrubs are always in flower, bearing scattered heads of white-starred blooms. The five-part flowers have yellow centres and quickly develop into bitter, green berries. Susumber plants are known throughout the Caribbean but Jamaicans are among the few that will eat the young fruit. These berries are cooked as an accompaniment to fish and meat dishes. Children, however try to be elsewhere when 'susumber' is served.

◆ **BIGNONIACEAE** *Calabash Tree family*

Garlic Vine (*Mansoa alliacea*, syn. *Pseudocalymma alliaceum*)
Other name Onion Vine

All parts of this popular, ornamental vine exude a faint odour of garlic. The scent intensifies when the leaves are crushed or bruised. The paired, compound leaves are a light, soft green. Each consists of only two, pointed leaflets. Near the ends of the branches there is a coiling green tendril in between each set of young leaflets. The vine spreads rapidly by flinging these tendrils everywhere to help support fast-growing stems. Several times a year, mature vines produce a spectacular, but short-lived froth of purplish bloom. The tubular flowers have a delicate, lavender-blue colour fading to white inside. As the flowers age, the colour pattern reverses until finally, the petals bleach, wither brown and die. The fruit are long, flattened, slender pods.

Pandorea (*Podranea ricasoliana*)
Other name Zimbabwe Creeper

Pandorea shrubs are African in origin. They are perennial, climbing plants that can scramble to great heights given suitable support. Their pinnate leaves are made up of nine to eleven, pointed, dark green leaflets. These have serrated edges and a lovely, silky smooth texture. Pandoreas are elegant, garden ornamentals that are widely grown in the cooler, mountain areas such as Mandeville. The plants flower on and off all year. At their peak, large specimens can cover entire walls and tall trees with bunches of pretty, sherbet-scented, pink blossom. Each bell-shaped flower has five, spreading petals and dark red lines which run way down into the white throat.

African Tulip Tree (*Spathodea campanulata*)
Other names Flame of the Forest, Fountain Tree

These West African forest trees have spread throughout the island. They are large, grey-barked and semi-deciduous and also seem to flourish particularly well in the higher, cooler districts. The trees routinely grow to an impressive 55 ft (17 m) and they remain in flower for a long time each year. The blooms are a striking scarlet, a colour that contrasts well with their large, dark green leaflets. Trees in full bloom can be easily spotted on far off hillsides. Each young, platter-sized inflorescence consists of an outer ring of open flowers, which surround dozens of closed, claw shaped buds. Popping these buds will release a squirt or fountain of water. A single flower is like a wobbly, five-lobed sac streaked yellow-red inside. Its five, free, crimson petal tips are delicately edged with gold. Even after flowering, the trees have a distinctive outline as their fruits are held above the leaves like extended fingers. The dried pods release large numbers of small, winged, heart-shaped seeds. Fruiting accomplished, the leaves are shed for a short period.

African Tulip Tree (*Spathodea campanulata*)

Yellow Poui (*Tabebuia chrysantha*)

Yellow Poui (*Tabebuia chrysantha*, syn. *T. rufescens*)

Yellow Pouis are medium-height, cultivated, ornamental trees that are native to Trinidad and South America. Their neat, lace-like foliage consists of tiers of small, light green, five-membered compound leaves. The trees flower spectacularly in spring, on bare branches, each leafless tree being transformed into one, blazing yellow, but short-lived inflorescence. The bloom consists of small, radiating groups of 2–2 ½ ins (5–6 cm) long, bell-shaped flowers. Within days, all that glory is shed to form a golden pond on the ground surrounding the bases of the trees. There is a much smaller, repeat flowering in September. *Tabebuia chrysantha* 'Araguaney' is the National Tree of Venezuela.

Pink Poui (*Tabebuia rosea*)

Pink Poui (*Tabebuia rosea*)

These tall, substantial trees are native to Mexico and northern South America. They are cultivated ornamentals here and are particularly common in urban Kingston and the Negril area. At maturity, *Tabebuia rosea* trees are clearly larger than their yellow-flowered relations. They may grow over 65 ft (20 m) tall and have upwardly slanting branches. The large, long-stemmed compound leaves have five leaflets arranged somewhat like the fingers of a hand. Pink Pouis flower from April to May, each individual tree being smothered tier by tier in bouquets of large, lavender-pink, bell-shaped flowers until the tree is one lovely riot of colour. Flowering is relatively short-lived. It lasts for a few weeks, diminishing slowly and making way for the returning, foliage. The trees flower again more sparingly in September. Wild species like the sweet smelling *T. angustata* and the endemic *T. riparia* (White Cedar) have light pink to white flowers. Many *Tabebuia* trees are excellent sources of hardwood.

Tabebuia rosea

Yellow Elder (*Tecoma stans*)

Although these shrubs and bushes grow all over the island, they are at their best in areas of disturbed limestone. Their pinnate leaves consist of three to nine, lance-shaped leaflets with saw-toothed edges. Bunches of long, slender fruit pods develop after flowering. *Tecoma* flowers are typical *Bignonia* bells – big, fragrant, blooms that are borne at the ends of the branches. These flaring, yellow flowers may grow up to 2 ins (5 cm) long and are marked with faint red lines running from throat to base. Mass flowering during late summer to spring can transform the waysides and hills into bright yellow plantations. The mountain slopes and roadsides between Kingston and Yallahs on the south-east coast are particularly good examples. For the rest of the year flowering is much less exuberant. Yellow Elder is native to Central and South America. It is also the National Flower of both the Bahamas and the US Virgin Islands. Unfortunately, this beautiful and easily grown flowering shrub is rarely seen in Jamaican gardens.

Yellow Elder Bush (*Tecoma stans*)

◆ ACANTHACEAE *Thunbergia family*

Asystasia (*Asystasia gangetica*)

Asystasias are now very common wild plants, which flower all year. They originated in the Old World tropics and pretty soon escaped from local gardens. The plants grow well in weedy, wasteland areas. After rain, roadsides can become alive with spikes of their pretty, upturned flowers. The creeping stems bear paired, oval leaves and upright, flowering stalks which each produce up to a dozen blooms that open in succession. All the flowers are attached to the same side of the stem. They come in a delightful range of soft colours, from pure white and pale yellows through pink blushes to lavender and purple. The tubular flowers, which are some $1\frac{1}{4}$–2 ins (3–5 cm) long, flare into five free petal tips. Sometimes the plants scramble thinly about, at other times they make sizeable, single-coloured clumps. They can also climb some way up into hedges, fences, bushes and trees.

Goldfussia (*Goldfussia glomerata*)

Goldfussia plants have come all the way from north-east India and Burma. They form scrambling, thicketing, 6ft (2 m) tall shrubs growing naturally in the damp, sheltered areas, between 2 300–5 600 ft (700–1 700 m) high up in the Blue Mountains. Both the foliage and the young stems are intensely hairy. The soft, paired leaves have toothed margins and prominent tips. However, one of the pair is always strikingly larger than the other. The shrubs bear clusters of beautiful, violet-blue flowers all year but the mass of tubular blossom is greatest in the cooler months. *Goldfussia colorata*, from the eastern Himalayas, bears small, pink blooms but has remarkable, two-toned foliage. The leaves are a dull green above but a glowing, red-purple underneath. Huge swathes of this rich vegetation now dominate hillsides and gullies around Hardwar Gap on the road from Kingston to Buff Bay.

Goldfussia glomerata

Red Cone-Flower (*Pachystachys spicata*, syn. *P. coccinea*)

Red Cone-Flowers are wild plants, which may have come from Guyana. They gather in abundance in moist mountain folds like those alongside the hilly section of Junction Road. The plants have running, rooting stems that can quickly establish a substantial colony. Their upright offshoots grow to about 3 ft (1 m) tall. They have large, hairy, paired leaves and bear small groups of erect flowering heads at the tips of the branches. Each inflorescence resembles a stiffened finger made up of rows of overlapping, green bracts. The striking, rich-red, tubular flowers are produced more or less all year. They emerge from behind the pointed, leafy bracts. Each curved bloom has three downward-pointing petals and an upright fourth that sheathes the golden stamens. Cone-Flowers also flourish in dry limestone hills such as above Ocho Rios. They grow on rough, stony, waste ground besides roads and near buildings. *Pachystachys lutea*, the Yellow Cone-Flower, is a popular garden shrub. It comes from Peru and has yellow bracts and white flowers.

Duppy Gun (*Ruellia tuberosa*)

After rain, low growing *Ruellia* plants seem to spring up everywhere. They appear at roadsides, in pastures, at the corners of playing fields and in many other open areas. This occurs because the plants have fleshy roots, which survive underground from season to season. The pretty, pint-sized plants bear paired leaves and remarkably large, bell-shaped blooms. Although the flowers are a beautiful bluish purple (rarely white) in colour they remain as weeds to the general public. The resulting fruits are small, seed-filled, torpedo-shaped pods. The name 'Duppy Gun' probably arose from the mini 'pop-pop' sounds made when the dry fruits are wetted by rain and split apart expelling the seeds. Children achieve the same effects by placing mature pods in water or in their mouths. Duppy gun plants do vary in form but the seedpods and persistent, spiky ring of five, long sepals is distinctive. Interestingly, *Ruellia* plants are also able to produce their 'guns' without first flowering.

Thunbergia (*Thunbergia grandiflora*)

Thunbergia grandiflora plants are very vigorous, climbing vines, which are native to India. They are grown to cover pergolas, tall walls, fences and other similar structures. The vines also thrive in the wild, in damp, woodland areas where their luxuriant growth can all but smother their hosts. These robust plants sport large, stiff leaves that have a scratchy feel. They vary in outline from smooth and heart-shaped to being lobed and more rectangular. Flowering is continuous and the hanging inflorescences are always crowded with sturdy buds and big, waxy blooms. The open flowers have tubular throats and wide, spreading corollas in shades of blue, purple or white. *Thunbergia alata* is the familiar, orange-coloured 'Black-eyed Susan' while *T. fragrans*, an equally slender vine, bears pure white, unscented blooms up to $1\frac{1}{2}$ ins (4 cm) wide. They both flower best in the cooler months of the year.

Thunbergia grandiflora

◆ **RUBIACEAE** *Coffee family*

Ixora (*Ixora coccinea*)

Red-flowered Ixoras, from tropical Asia, are the commonest of this group of hugely popular ornamentals. They are sturdy garden shrubs that have glossy leaves and long-lasting heads of massed, tubular florets. There are a variety of forms including double or single-flowered, miniature or full-sized, plus a range of colours, which go from pink through to orange and fragrant white. Ixoras flower throughout the year. They are highly drought-resistant and need little attention beyond occasional pruning. An added bonus is that the massive flower heads are regular stops for butterflies and hummingbirds refuelling on the wing.

Ixora (*Ixora coccinea*)

Mussaenda (*Mussaenda erythrophylla*)

Pink Mussaendas are staple items in gardens seen very commonly, for instance in surburban Kingston. The shrubs have stiff, felty leaves and produce a profusion of bright, blowsy, pink flower heads. The blooms are really enlarged bracts that billow up and around the small, orange-yellow corolla tubes. They are also available in shades of red, orange, yellow and white and in single or double forms. The plants are sensitive to lack of water and will wilt severely at the first signs of drought. Mussaendas are of African or Asiatic origin.

Bell Flower (*Portlandia grandiflora*)

Portlandia is a genus of six endemic species that bear white or crimson flowers. These glossy-leaved shrubs are common on rocky limestone cliffs from sea level up to about 2100 ft (650 m). Some grow into small, floriferous trees. *Portlandia grandiflora* is the most commonly found and is also blessed with the largest blooms. The startlingly white, waxy corollas range from 4–8 ins (10–20 cm) in length and are poised more or less horizontally. These beautiful, fragrant flowers are produced throughout the year and they contrast well with the lustrous, dark green, paired foliage. The fruits of *P. grandiflora* are oval capsules that can grow up to 1 in (2.5 cm) long. For all these facts and more, Bell Flower shrubs are fast becoming garden items.

Hot Lips (*Psychotria elata,* syn. *Cephaelis elata*)

Psychotria elata is a voluptuous, endemic plant that grows in moist, upland regions of the eastern parishes. Together, the plants form part of the understorey in the forests of the Blue Mountains and grow at altitudes of between 1100–5000 ft (330–1500 m). The shrubs are generally 6–10 ft (2–3 m) tall and bear bunches of paired, gleaming green leaves on brittle branches. The young stems in particular are ringed like the joints of a bamboo. Flowering starts with the appearance of fleshy, greenish bracts. These develop more pairs within pairs of bracts and they become progressively brighter-coloured. The outermost, largest two bracts are outrageous, crimson, heart-shaped structures – the 'Hot Lips'. The bract pairs also enclose the short-lived, real flowers, which are simple, white tubes. Hot Lips flower dramatically from December to August during which time small fruits are also produced.

◆ **ASTERACEAE** *Daisy family*

Spanish Needle (*Bidens pilosa*)

There are about seven Spanish Needle species present in Jamaica and four are endemic. They are exceedingly common tropical weeds – one sort or another occurring in all possible wasteland areas from sea level up to about 5 000 ft (1 500 m). The plants range in height from prostrate to chest high. *Bidens pilosa* is a well-branched, annual weed that can maintain a good crop of hairy, green leaves throughout the dry season. The plants are often the only green things in a brown lawn providing a snack for hungry, stray cattle and pickings for caged pet rabbits and guinea pigs. Spanish Needle plants have also been eaten as spinach. The pretty daisy-type flowers are produced continuously. Each long-stemmed, composite flower is about $\frac{1}{2}$ in (1 cm) wide and consists of an outer ring of white petals surrounding a yellow centre. The small, hooked fruits have considerable nuisance value as they so easily become attached to skin and clothing.

Jamaican Marigold (*Sphagneticola trilobata,* syn. *Wedelia trilobata*)

The orange-yellow, daisy heads of Jamaican Marigolds bloom from sandy beaches right up to mountainside road banks and clearings. These plants prefer damp places where their creeping, rooting stems and dark green foliage can form substantial mats. The paired leaves are toothed, strongly three-lobed and so bristly as to make rasping sounds when stroked. Flowers spring singly from the axils of the leaves and are borne on top of extra long (up to 6 ins (15 cm)) stalks. These blooms are $1-1\frac{1}{2}$ ins (2–3 cm) wide and can be seen all year round. This species is also found in other West Indian islands, tropical America, West Africa and Hawaii.

Glossary

Annual   plant that lives for one year or growing season only

Axil   angle made by leaf or branch with the stem

Bract   small, leaf-like structure directly beneath, but separate from, the flower

Calyx   (pl. calyces) group or ring of sepals

Compound   leaf made up of smaller units called leaflets

Corolla   group or ring of petals

Dicotyledon   major group of plants whose embryos have two seed leaves or cotyledons

Duppy   ghost or spirit

Endemic   describes a plant that is not native anywhere else

Epiphyte   plant that grows on another plant (host) for support only

Floret   one of a cluster of tiny flowers

Floriferous   bearing many flowers

Fused   joined

Indigenous   native to a particular region, not introduced

Inflorescence   flowers that share a common stem

Macca   prickle, thorn or sharp spine

Monocotyledon   major group of plants whose embryos have one seed leaf or cotyledon

Perennial   plant that lives for several years or growing seasons

Pinnate   compound leaves, as illustrated below

Pinnate (once, odd) 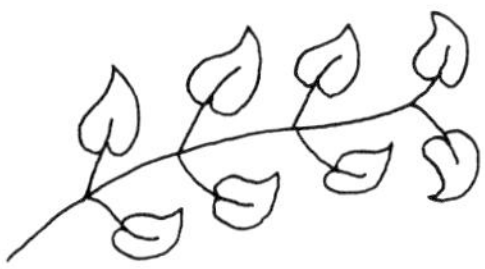   Pinnate (once, even)

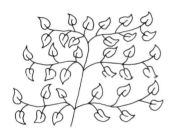

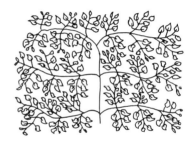

Bi-pinnate (even)
Twice pinnate
Doubly pinnate

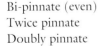

Tri-pinnate (even)
Triply pinnate

Sepal   leaf-like structure that protects a bud and persists at the base of the flower

Species   (spp.) distinct types of plants; different species do not normally interbreed

Succulent   fleshy and juicy inside

Toxic   poisonous

Variant   a form of plant that differs very little from the described species

Whorls   describes leaves (and other things) that are arranged in rings

Xerophyte/Xerophytic   plant that normally lives in (hot) dry conditions

Bibliography

Adams, C.D. (1972) *Flowering Plants of Jamaica*, University of the West Indies, Mona, Jamaica

Bannochie, I. and Light, M. (1993) *Gardening in the Caribbean*, Macmillan Education Ltd., London and Basingstoke

Berry, Fred and Kress, W. John (1991) *Heliconia: An Identification Guide*, Smithsonian Institution Press

Carrington, S. (1998) *Wild Plants of the Eastern Caribbean*, Macmillan Education Ltd.

Foggi, B. and Innocenti, A. (2001) *Flowers of the Caribbean*, Casa Editrice Bonechi/LMH Publishing

Hawkes, A.D. and Sutton, B.C. (1974) *Wild Flowers of Jamaica*, Collins Sangster

Lennox, G.W. and Seddon, A. (1978) *Flowers of the Caribbean*, Macmillan Education Ltd., London and Basingstoke

Robertson, D. (1988 Reprint) *Jamaican Herbs*, Jamaican Herbs Ltd.

Webster, A. (1986) *Caribbean Gardening*, United Co-op. Printers Ltd.

Index of Common Names

Index of Botanical Names

– splendens. See *Euphorbia milii.*

Furcraea hexapetala, 19
Gliricidia sepium, **53**
Goldfussia colorata, 125
– glomerata, **125**
Gossypium barbadense, 72
Guaiacum officinale, **56**

Hedychium coronarium, 12
– gardnerianum, 13
Heliconia psittacorum, 9, 10
– rostrata, **9**
– spp., 9
– wagneriana, 10
Hibiscus elatus, 67
– esculentus, 68
– malvaviscus. See *Malvaviscus arboreus.*
– rosa-sinensis, 69, 71
– sabdariffa, 70
– schizopetalus, 71
Hippeastrum puniceum, 17
Holmskioldia sanguinea, 105
Hymenocallis latifolia, 18

Ipomoea fistulosa, **99**
Ixora coccinea, **129**

Jatropha integerrima, **64**
– multifida, 65
– podagrica, **65**

Kalanchoe pinnatum. See *Bryophyllum pinnatum.*

Lagerstroemia indica, **79,** 80
– speciosa, **80**
Lantana camara, **106**
Lisianthius longifolius, 87
Ludwigia octovalvis, 84

Malvaviscus arboreus, 73

– var. penduliflorus, 73
Mangifera indica, 24
Mansoa alliacea, **114**
Millettia spp., **54**
Mimosa pudica, **43**
Mirabilis jalapa, 27
Momordica charantia, 78
Murraya paniculata, **59**
Mussaenda erythrophylla, **131**

Nerium oleander, **91**

Pachystachy spicata, **126**
– coccinea, **126**
– lutea, 126
Parkinsonia aculeata, **39**
Peltophorum pterocarpum, **40**
Pentalinon luteum. See *Urechites lutea.*
Petrea volubilis, **107**
Plumbago auriculata, **86**
– capensis, 86
– scandens, 86
Plumeria obtusa, 92
– rubra, **92**
Podranea ricasoliana, **115**
Portlandia grandiflora, **132**
Pseudocalymma alliaceum. See *Mansoa alliacea.*
Psychotria elata, **133**
Punica granatum, **81**

Quisqualis indica, **82**

Ricinus communis, **66**
Ruellia tuberosa, **127**

Salvia coccinea, **108**
Samanea saman, **44,** **45**
Schefflera actinophylla, **85**
– sciadophyllum, 85
Sechium edule, **97**
Solandra grandiflora, **111**